NEW *ILLUSTRATED* ENCYCLOPEDIA OF GARDENING

UNABRIDGED

WILD FLOWERS OF AMERICA

GREYSTONE PRESS/NEW YORK · TORONTO · LONDON

The full color plates in this volume are based on "North American Wild Flowers," a portfolio of paintings by Mary Vaux Walcott, as published by the Smithsonian Institution of Washington, with supplementary paintings (plates marked DFP) by Dorothy Falcon Platt.

Introduction

The full color paintings reproduced in this book are a selection from the beauty and interest of North American wild flowers. From the thousands of kinds of flowering plants which grow wild on the continent (and we do not yet know all of them), these were chosen for various reasons: some because they are hard to find — like those which frequent the upper slopes of the highest mountains; some because of their gorgeous colors or curious shapes — like Cardinal Flower and Lady's-slipper; some because everyone knows them — like Goldenrod and Buttercup. They range from the everlasting snows to tropic swamps, from woods to deserts. The Orchids, with their curious and often beautiful flowers, are well represented; so are those curious plants which catch insects and are nourished by them. Certain groups of exceptional beauty, like the Mariposa Lilies and the Gentians, are also fully treated.

In speaking of plants, the botanist finds it necessary to use technical names for them rather than the common names of spoken language; and the interested layman soon finds that it is best for him also to become familiar with botanical names, forbidding as they may seem at first sight. Plate 7 for instance, illustrates a plant commonly known as Western Red Cedar. The name Cedar has unfortunately been used for several trees superficially more or less alike but only distantly related. Western Red Cedar is closely related to Arbor Vitae, but not to the Red Cedar of the eastern states. The White Cedar is distinct from all these plants, and the Cedars of the Old World, including Cedar of Lebanon, are again only distantly related to them and do not even much resemble them. The Bluebells of Scotland (see Plate 181) are in a different family from English Bluebells, and neither is related to some of the many American plants called Bluebells (Plate 158, for example). The Spring Beauty of one midwestern state is called Hepatica in another, where the name Spring Beauty is used for a quite different flower. And so we might multiply examples of the confusion inherent in colloquial names, without even drawing attention to the fact that all such names are useless as soon as we pass into a country in which English is not spoken.

Botanical names are really quite simple; they are based on the classification of plants. All the plants of one sort which grow wild form a population we call a species; all the white pines compose one species, all the limber pines another. Similar species, having certain main characters in common, form a genus; all pines — white, red, yellow, limber, and so on — are in one genus. Each genus (the plural is genera) has a name formed of a single word, usually a Latin noun: *Pinus, Rosa, Delphinium* are the names of genera. Many names of genera are in everyday use, especially by gardeners: *Begonia, Phlox, Gladiolus, Scilla, Narcissus, Chrysanthemum, Zinnia* are all names of genera. The name of a species is formed of two words, the first being the name of the genus to which it belongs, the second a qualifying word, usually a Latin adjective. *Pinus flexilis, Rosa carolina, Delphinium elongatum, Phlox divaricata* are the names of species. Within species the botanist often distinguishes groups set off by less evident differences (slight differences in form or color, for instance); such groups may be called subspecies, varieties, or forms, and are named by adding further qualifying words to the name of the species. Going in the other direction, we arrange genera in larger groups called families. Each family is named by a single word usually ending in -aceae: Pinaceae, Rosaceae, Geraniaceae are names of families. The families again compose the larger groups of the plant kingdom.

Two of these larger groups are represented in this book, the conifers and the flowering plants. The two groups are similar in many ways, the cones of the first resembling the flowers of the second in essential features; so that it is proper to include both in a work entitled *Wild Flowers of America*. The cones of conifers are composed of scales arranged spirally around a central stem. There are two kinds of cones. The scales of one kind form pollen in small sacs attached to their under surface; this pollen, when it is liberated in the spring, may appear as a visible yellow cloud. The scales which form pollen are called stamens, and the cones composed of stamens are staminate cones. They usually grow in clusters, and wither away after the pollen is shed (see Plates 5,6).

The other kind of cone (Plates 1, 4) bears on its scales minute bodies called ovules, which, when fertilized by the pollen, become the seeds; these cones are called ovulate cones. As the seeds ripen, the cones become larger and usually more or less woody; the scales finally spread apart and the seeds attached to them fall out.

The essential parts of a flower are stamens and pistils; these are usually present in the same flower, though some species have distinct staminate and pistillate flowers. The stamens form pollen, like those of the conifers; each consists usually of an oblong head on a narrow stalk (well shown in Plates 20,22). The stamens surround the pistil or pistils. The pistil consists of a hollow lower part, the ovary, which contains one or more ovules, and above this a style supporting a stigma on which the pollen is deposited (or several styles and stigmas); the pistil is clearly seen in Plates 20 and 135. These parts are in most flowers surrounded by the perianth, which is composed commonly of two rings or cycles of parts, an outer ring of sepals, which are often green, and an inner ring of petals, which may be brightly colored and of complex form (see, for instance, the Trillium in Plate 29). However, the two rings of parts may be all alike or nearly so, as in the Lily shown in Plate 21, in which case the terms sepals and petals are not used; or there may be only one ring of parts, as in the Anemone shown in Plate 65, in which case they are arbitrarily called sepals.

All the parts of the flower are attached to the tip of the flower-stalk, which is commonly expanded into a knob, a disc, or a cup, and is referred to as the receptacle. When it is cup-shaped or urn-shaped, as in a Rose (see Plate 94), the pistil or pistils occupy the inside of the cup, the stamens and perianth being attached to its margin. In many flowers the ovary is not only within a cup-shaped receptacle, it is so embedded in it that it cannot be detached; one cannot say where the ovary leaves off and the receptacle begins. This sort of ovary is spoken of as inferior. It is not easy to demonstrate in a painting of a flower, but in Blue-eyed Grass (Plate 34) it may be seen that the tip of the flower-stalk is swollen just below the blue perianth; this part contains the inferior ovary.

The pollen received by the stigma sends its pollen tubes into the pistil and fertilizes the ovules therein.

As the ovules develop into seeds, the surrounding ovary also enlarges and changes in structure, becoming the fruit. This is the essential difference between cones and flowers: in cones the seeds are attached to the surface of the parts that bear them; in flowers they are enclosed in a hollow structure. Other parts of the flower may be involved in the formation of the fruit, particularly if the ovary is inferior.

The first two families treated in this book are conifers; the rest are flowering plants.

The brief descriptions given are intended to call attention to the principal features which distinguish a species from its relatives, except those which are clearly evident in the illustrations. It is obviously impossible, without a much more detailed and technical treatment, to provide a means of identification for all North American wild flowers. The heights given are usually the maximum heights to which the species may grow; but when this is shown in the paintings (which are all life-size) it is not mentioned in the descriptions. The plants come from all over the North American continent north of Mexico (and a few extend south of the boundary). Some idea is given of the habitat of each species, that is, the kind of situation in which it is found. Some plants are so widely distributed that it is difficult to say anything of their preferences in soil, moisture and shade. Others are designated simply as "arctic," which means that they grow where the ground is frozen most of the year; or "alpine," when they frequent the rocky slopes or mountain meadows above timberline.

— H. W. RICKETT

The Mary Vaux Walcott color plates in this book are reproduced by permission from the famous portfolio set "North American Wild Flowers," by Mary Vaux Walcott, as published by the Smithsonian Institution.

Glossary

Achene: A small dry fruit containing one seed, and not splitting open at maturity; see Buttercup, Sunflower.

Basal: At the base; of leaves growing at the base of the stem, as those of Saxifrage; of the lower parts of petals, sepals, etc.

Beard: A tuft of hairs, as on the petal of Pogonia.

Berry: A fruit which is succulent throughout.

Bracts: Leaves associated with flowers, usually smaller than the other leaves, as in Phlox, Tar-flower; often differently shaped or colored, as in *Monarda, Castilleia;* also associated with the scales of ovulate cones.

Bud-scales: Scales which enclose a dormant bud, usually falling when the bud opens.

Capsule: A pod containing seeds enclosed in several chambers or attached in several rows, and splitting open into several parts at maturity; found in Lilies, Violets, and many others.

Catkin: An often pendent branch of small flowers which usually lack petals and either stamens or pistils, as in Willows and Alders.

Chaff: In this book, applied to the bracts associated with the disc-flowers of the Composite Family.

Claw: The narrow stalk by which some petals are attached.

Column: The peculiar structure in the center of an orchid flower, composed of style, stigma and one or two stamens joined together; see p. 53.

Corm: A bulbous underground stem, as in Trillium.

Crest: A ridge or protrusion, especially on petals, as in Milkwort, Squirrel Corn.

Crown: A ring formed by outgrowths from the perianth, as in Daffodils (where it forms the "trumpet") and Milkweed.

Epiphyte: A plant which grows attached to another plant but does not draw its nourishment from it, as *Epidendrum.*

Falls: See p. 47.

Gland: A body which exudes some substance, such as oil or nectar; also used of bodies which have the appearance of glands.

Glaucous: Grayish-green with a waxy surface.

Inferior ovary: An ovary imbedded in the receptacle; see p. 5.

Involucre: A circle of bracts usually beneath a flower-cluster, as in *Anemone deltoidea, Pulsatilla,* the Composite Family.

Irregular flower: A flower which is not radially symmetrical, the upper parts differing from the lower; see the Orchid and Mint Families.

Keel: The two lower petals of the flower of the Bean Family, joined by their lower edges to form a boat-shaped body; also a similar body in the flower of Milkwort.

Lip: The lower petal of an orchid flower, usually much larger than the others and of a different shape; see also two-lipped.

Nectar: A sweet liquid formed in flowers.

Nectar-gland, nectary: A body which exudes nectar, found in various positions in flowers.

Ovary: The lower part of a pistil, which contains the ovules; see p. 5.

Ovule: The rudiment of a seed.

Palate: A projection on the lower lip of some two-lipped flowers which closes the opening or nearly so, as in Toadflax.

Palmately: Spreading like the fingers of a hand; referring to leaf-segments, as those of Lupine, Buckeye.

Papilionaceous: Butterfly-like; referring to the type of flower characteristic of the Bean Family (p. 103).

Pappus: A structure which replaces sepals in the individual flowers of the Composite Family; often composed of small scales or bristles (see p. 193).

Parasite: A plant (or animal) which is attached to another plant (or animal) and takes its nourishment directly from it, as Mistletoe, Cancer-root.

Perianth: The part of a flower which surrounds the stamens and pistil; its parts are of a great variety of shapes, often brightly colored; see p. 5.

Pinnately: Arranged in two ranks along the sides of a stalk, as the leaf-segments of Vetch.

Pistil: The central part of a flower (or there may be several); the lower part usually enlarges and forms the case (fruit) around the seeds; see p. 4.

Plumose: Feathery.

Pod: A dry fruit which opens when ripe; capsule.

Pollen: A dust-like or sticky mass made up of minute grains, commonly yellow, formed in the head of a stamen (see p. 4).

Pollinium: A mass of cohering pollen grains found in Orchids and Milkweeds.

Pseudobulb: A thickened branch of an Orchid containing food and water.

Receptacle: The end of the flower-stalk to which the parts of the flower are attached; often expanded, cup-shaped in a Cherry blossom, urn-shaped in a Rose, cushion-like in a Strawberry.

Sepals: The outer parts of the perianth when this is composed of two rings, as in Buttercups; equivalent to perianth when the parts of the latter are all alike, as in Anemone; see p. 5.

Spadix: The thick branch on which the flowers of the Arum Family are borne (p. 21).

Spathe: The large bract which encloses the spadix of the Arum Family (p. 21); also used of any large bract or group of bracts, as in Blue-eyed Grass.

Spur: A hollow projection or tubular extension usually of a petal, as in Violet, Columbine.

Stamen: The part of a flower which forms the pollen; the stamens are situated within the perianth and around the pistil or pistils; each consists commonly of a stalk and head; see p. 4.

Standard: The upper petal of the characteristic flower of the Bean Family; also a sepal of an Iris.

Stellate: Star-shaped, having radiating arms; many plant hairs, as those of Bladderpod, Scarlet Globe-mallow, may be seen through a magnifier to have radiating branches.

Stigma: The uppermost part of the pistil, which receives the pollen.

Stipules: Paired appendages, often like small leaves or leaf-segments, at the base of a leaf-stalk; as in Rose.

Style: The slender part of the pistil which rises from the ovary and bears the stigma.

Tendril: A slender clasping or coiling structure, usually a special branch or a part of a leaf, by which some plants attach themselves to supporting objects; see Vetch.

Tuber: An underground enlarged stem or root or portion thereof in which food, such as starch or sugar, accumulates; see Rue Anemone.

Tubercle: A small enlargement, as at the base of the hairs of some Sunflowers.

Two-lipped: Petals or sepals which are united to form a tube may spread at the end into unequal upper and lower lips; see *Chelone, Monarda.*

Umbel: A flower-cluster, roughly resembling an umbrella, in which all the stalks radiate from one point; see Bird's-eye Primrose.

Valve: One of the parts into which a capsule splits at maturity.

Whorl: A ring or cycle of parts; referring to leaves, petals, etc.

Wing: A flattened extension of a fruit, as in Maples; one of the lateral petals of the papilionaceous flower of the Bean Family.

READY IDENTIFICATION CHART

This chart provides a convenient means for identifying the wild flowers shown in this book. There are, however, thousands of other species which grow wild in North America. If a plant can be fitted into one of the classes shown in the chart, it may probably be referred to one of the corresponding families or genera, or to one of their relatives. In this way the search for the precise species is narrowed down considerably.

For the technical terms used in the chart, the reader is referred to the Glossary on page 6.

I. The cone-bearing plants, all woody, with narrow leaves which are often needle-like and which mostly remain on the plant through the winter (the exception is *Larix*).

Pine and Cypress Families.

II. The flowering plants, woody and herbaceous, with leaves of various shapes but rarely needle-like and mostly falling in the autumn. See A-O below.

A. Plants lacking green color.
> Monotropa
> Hypopitys
> Orobanche
> Conopholis

B. Plants growing attached to other plants and lacking contact with the ground (parasites and epiphytes).
> Tillandsia
> Epidendrum
> Cyrtopodium
> Phoradendron

C. Plants growing in water (the flowers emerging).
> Sagittaria
> Pontederia
> Water-lily Family
> Menyanthes

D. Prickly cushion-like cacti. Cactus Family

E. Orchids, with the lower petal (the lip) usually large and differently shaped and/or colored from the others, and the stamen(s) united with the style and stigma. Orchid Family

F. Herbaceous plants with leaves shaped like pitchers or vases, in which insects are trapped.
Pitcher-plant Family

G. Herbaceous plants with small flowers crowded in a thick spike which is generally enveloped by a single large leaf; the latter is often colored and may be mistaken for a petal. Arum Family

H. Grass-like plants with small flowers lacking obvious perianth and crowded together in scaly clusters.
Sedge Family

I. Herbaceous plants with small flowers gathered in heads which simulate flowers; in one head the actual flowers are tubular or strap-shaped or both (the latter then forming rays around a central disc).
Composite Family

J. Shrubs or small trees, without colored perianth, their flowers in catkins. *Salix* and *Alnus*

K. Herbaceous and woody plants with papilionaceous flowers and leaves mostly divided into leaflets.
part of Bean Family

L. Vines, climbing by tendrils attached to other plants or to fences, etc., or by twining around them.
> Clematis
> Wisteria
> Vicia
> Lathyrus
> Passiflora
> Gelsemium
> Campsis
> Anisostichus
> Lonicera

8

M. Woody plants (trees and shrubs), with flowers of various types, other than those in J-L. See 1-23 below.

	LEAVES	PERIANTH	STAMENS	PISTIL(S)	
1.	attached singly, often large.	large white or greenish sepals.	many.	many.	Magnolia Family
2.	attached singly.	3 green sepals, 6 brown-purple petals.	many.	several.	*Asimina*
3.	attached singly, usually with stipules; often divided.	about 5 sepals, 5 petals.	many.	one or more in a head or in a cup-shaped receptacle.	part of Rose Family
4.	attached singly.	about 5 sepals, 5 petals.	many.	one, with inferior ovary.	Apple Family
5.	attached singly.	4 sepals, 5 petals.	many.	one.	Tea Family
6.	attached singly.	5 sepals, often minute, 5 petals.	5.	one, with inferior ovary.	*Ribes* *Oplopanax*
7.	attached singly.	4 sepals, 4 strap-shaped narrow petals.	8.	one, with 2 styles.	*Hamamelis*
8.	attached in pairs.	4 small colored sepals, no petals.	8.	one.	*Shepherdia*
9.	attached singly, each pinnately divided.	6 sepals, 6 petals, several bracts, all small, yellow.	6.	one, becoming a blue berry.	*Mahonia*
10.	attached singly.	4-6 sepals, 4-8 petals, all small.	as many as petals.	one, becoming a red or black berry.	*Ilex*
11.	attached singly, often lobed.	5 sepals, 5 large petals, several bracts.	many, all joined in a column around the style.	one, with 5-branched style.	*Hibiscus*
12.	attached singly, silvery or evergreen.	4 or 5 yellow sepals, no petals.	as many as sepals.	one.	*Elaeagnus* *Fremontia*
13.	attached singly, evergreen.	2 sepals, 4 yellow petals.	many.	one.	*Dendromecon*
14.	attached singly, small.	5 sepals, often minute, 5 petals joined to form a hanging cup or urn.	8-10.	one, with inferior ovary, becoming a berry.	Blueberry Family
15.	attached singly or sometimes in pairs or whorls, or basal or crowded.	4 or 5 sepals, 4 or 5 petals joined at the base.	5-10.	one.	Heath Family Diapensia Family
16.	attached singly, needle-like.	3 sepals, no petals.	3.	one, becoming berry-like.	*Empetrum*
17.	attached in pairs, palmately divided.	5 sepals, 4 or 5 unequal petals.	7.	one, becoming a tough round pod.	*Aesculus*
18.	attached in pairs, palmately lobed.	5 sepals, 5 petals, all small.	3-6.	one, 2-lobed, becoming a winged "key."	*Acer*
19.	attached in pairs.	4 sepals, 4 petals joined at base; cluster of flowers sometimes surrounded by petal-like bracts.	4.	one, with inferior ovary, becoming a berry-like fruit.	part of Dogwood Family
20.	attached in pairs.	4 sepals, 4 petals joined at base.	4.	one, becoming a purplish fruit.	*Callicarpa*

	LEAVES	PERIANTH	STAMENS	PISTIL(S)	
21.	attached in pairs.	5 small sepals, 5 petals joined at base.	5.	one, with inferior ovary, becoming a berry.	part of Honeysuckle Family
22.	attached in pairs.	4 minute sepals, 4 strap-shaped petals joined at base.	2.	one, becoming an olive-like fruit.	*Chionanthus*
23.	bunched above spines of stem.	5 sepals, 5 red petals, partly joined.	10 or more.	one, becoming a small pod.	*Fouquieria*

N. Herbaceous plants other than those in A-I and K, and having separate petals or no petals (sometimes the sepals resemble petals). See 1-18 below.

	LEAVES	PERIANTH	STAMENS	PISTIL(S)	
1.	attached singly or in whorls, or basal.	6 parts, all alike or 3 green, 3 colored.	6.	one, becoming a berry or 3-chambered pod.	Lily Family *Tradescantia*
2.	chiefly basal, narrow or even grass-like.	6 parts, all more or less alike in color.	3 or 6.	one, with inferior ovary, becoming a 3-chambered pod.	Amaryllis and Iris Families,
3.	attached singly.	5 green sepals, no petals.	5.	one, with 1 or 2 styles.	*Comandra* *Chenopodium*
4.	basal, heart-shaped on stalks.	3 brown sepals, no petals.	12.	one, with inferior ovary.	*Asarum*
5.	attached singly or basal, often palmately lobed or divided.	about 5 sepals, 5 petals or none; sometimes spurred.	many.	rarely one, usually several on a projecting receptacle.	part of Buttercup Family
6.	attached singly.	4 sepals, 4 petals.	6, 4 longer than the other 2.	one, becoming a pod.	Mustard Family
7.	attached singly or basal.	5 sepals, 5 petals.	5 or 10.	one, becoming a 1- to 5-chambered pod.	part of Saxifrage Family, *Cassia* *Geranium*
8.	attached singly or basal, often lobed or divided, with stipules.	5 sepals, 5 petals.	many.	several or many, in a cup-shaped or on a projecting receptacle.	part of Rose Family
9.	attached singly, with stipules.	5 sepals, 5 petals, often 3 bracts.	many, joined in a column around the style.	one, with about 5 branches of the style.	part of Mallow Family
10.	attached singly or basal.	5 sepals, 5 petals, the lowest spurred.	5, cohering around the style.	one, becoming a pod with many seeds in one chamber.	Violet Family
11.	attached in pairs.	5 sepals, 5 petals.	10.	one, with 3-5 styles.	Pink Family
12.	attached in pairs.	2 sepals, 5 petals.	5.	one, with 3 styles or a 3-branched style.	Purslane Family
13.	one pair or basal.	4-6 sepals, 6-9 petals.	8 or more.	one.	part of Barberry Family
14.	attached singly or basal.	2 sepals, soon falling, 4-12 petals.	many.	one, becoming a pod.	Poppy Family
15.	attached singly.	3 sepals, the lower yellow, much inflated and spurred; 3 petals.	5.	one, becoming a pod which opens explosively.	*Impatiens*
16.	attached in pairs.	5 sepals, 5 yellow petals.	many, often in several bunches.	one, with several styles.	*Hypericum*

		LEAVES	PERIANTH	STAMENS	PISTIL(S)	
17.		basal, folding along the midrib, the toothed edges interlocking, to trap insects.	5 sepals, 5 petals.	10-20, joined at base.	one.	*Dionaea*
18.		basal, long-stalked.	3 sepals, 3 petals.	many, in separate flowers from pistils.	many, in separate flowers from stamens.	*Sagittaria* PL. 12.

O. Herbaceous plants other than those in A–I, K and N, having petals united at least at their bases (if one petal is pulled off carefully, all of them come off together) or at their tips. See 1–14 below.

	LEAVES	PERIANTH	STAMENS	PISTIL(S)	
1.	attached singly or basal, delicately cut.	2 sepals, soon falling, 4 petals joined at tips, 1 or 2 spurred.	6, joined in 2 bunches.	one, becoming a pod.	Fumitory Family
2.	attached singly, narrow.	5 sepals, 2 bearing wings, 3 petals, 1 crested.	6 or 8, joined in 2 sets.	one.	*Polygala*
3.	attached singly or in pairs or whorls.	4 sepals, 4 petals.	4 or 8.	one, with inferior ovary, becoming a narrow pod or a berry-like fruit.	Evening Primrose Family part of Dogwood Family Madder Family
4.	chiefly basal.	5 sepals, 5 petals, joined at base.	10.	one.	part of Wintergreen Family
5.	basal.	5 sepals, 5 petals, their tips spreading or reflexed.	5, attached to the petals.	one.	Primrose Family
6.	attached in pairs.	5 sepals, 5 petals, often pleated, all twisted together in bud.	5.	one, becoming a pod with many seeds in one chamber.	part of Gentian Family
7.	attached in pairs.	5 sepals, 5 petals, all reflexed, with a crown.	5, attached to the stigma.	one, becoming a pod; the seeds bearing silky hairs.	*Asclepias*
8.	attached in pairs.	5 sepals, 5 petals forming a tube with flaring lobes.	5, attached to the petals.	one, three-chambered.	Phlox Family
9.	attached singly.	5 sepals, 5 petals, joined near base.	5, attached to the petals.	one, 2- or 4-chambered.	Waterleaf and Borage Families
10.	attached in pairs.	5 sepals, 5 petals forming 2 lips.	2, or 4 in 2 pairs of unequal length.	one, 4-lobed.	part of Verbena Family Mint Family
11.	attached singly, in pairs or whorls, or basal.	5 sepals, 5 petals forming 2 lips.	2 or 4, attached to the petals (a rudimentary fifth stamen sometimes present).	one, 2-chambered.	Figwort Family *Pinguicula*
12.	attached in pairs.	5 sepals, 5 petals nearly alike.	3 or 4.	one, with inferior ovary.	*Linnaea* *Valeriana*
13.	attached singly or basal.	5 sepals, 5 petals forming a bell.	5.	one, with inferior ovary.	*Campanula*
14.	attached singly.	5 sepals, 5 petals forming a tube split on the upper side and ending in 2 upper and 3 lower teeth.	5.	one, with inferior ovary.	*Lobelia*

Conifers. Coniferae

Pine family. Pinaceae

PINE *PINUS*

The pines are distinguished by having their leaves in small clusters on spur-like lateral shoots, much as the larches do; the needles are longer than those of the larches and fewer in a cluster, and remain on the tree for several years. They are our most valuable sources of lumber. There are many species, occurring all over the northern hemisphere.

Cypress family. Cupressaceae

Alpine Fir *Abies lasiocarpa* **Pl. 1.**

The firs may be distinguished by their erect cones. Their leaves are mostly flat and blunt, without stalks; when they fall, they leave the branches smooth. The bark forms abundant liquid resin in blister-like pockets.

Alpine Fir is a pyramidal tree reaching 100 feet and more in height, with leaves 1 to 1¾ inches long. The cones are 2½ to 4 inches long when mature. The wood is light, weak, of little value.

A related species is the Balsam Fir of the northeastern states, much used for Christmas trees.

Alpine Fir grows on high mountain slopes up to timberline, from Montana to Washington and Alaska, and southward to northern New Mexico and Arizona. The specimen illustrated came from Bow Pass, near the boundary of Alberta and British Columbia, at an altitude of 6,000 feet.

Douglas Fir *Pseudotsuga taxifolia* Pl. 2.
This tree is called the false hemlock (Pseudotsuga) because its leaves are stalked like those of hemlocks and its cones droop from the ends of the branches. It has also been called fir because of its pitch-pockets, and spruce because of the arrangement of its leaves. In the structure of its cones, however, it differs from all these trees. A distinctive feature is the two-lobed, long-pointed bracts which project between the seed-bearing scales.

This species is a large tree, often reaching 200 feet in height (and sometimes over 300 feet), with soft, flat leaves ¾ to 1¼ inches long. The cones are 2 to 4 inches long. It is a valuable source of lumber.

Douglas Fir grows from sea level to high altitudes, from Wyoming southward to western Texas and northern Mexico, and westward to the Pacific Coast in British Columbia, Washington and Oregon and to the Sierra Nevada in California (but absent from the dry mountain ranges of the Great Basin). The illustration was made from a branch obtained near Radium Hot Springs in the Columbia River Valley, British Columbia, at an altitude of 3,000 feet.

Western Larch *Larix occidentalis* Pl. 3
Larches differ from other conifers in shedding their leaves every winter. The short, needle-like leaves grow in clusters on spur-like shoots which arise from the branches.

This species may reach 200 feet in height; the branches are long and slender. The leaves are 1 to 2 inches long, 3-angled in section, from 14 to 30 in a cluster. The cones are small (1 to 1½ inches long) and grow thickly along the branches.

A related species is the Tamarack of northeastern swampy forests.

Western Larch grows at altitudes of 2,000·to 7,000 feet from Montana to British Columbia and southward to northern Idaho, northeastern Oregon and the Columbia River. The branch illustrated came from Horse Thief River, British Columbia, at an altitude of 3,000 feet.

Limber Pine *Pinus flexilis* Pl. 4.

This is usually a small tree or even a shrub, stunted by the rigorous conditions of the high mountains where it grows. The leaves grow 5 to a spur and are 2 to 3 inches long. The cones are 4 to 10 inches long. The illustration shows, at the extreme tip of the branch, young ovulate cones ready for pollen; as the branch continues its growth, these will bend aside and grow to be like the year-old cone below.

Limber Pine grows near timberline from South Dakota to Alberta and southward to western Texas, New Mexico and California. The specimen sketched grew near Lake Minnewonka, Alberta, at an altitude of 4,000 feet.

Long-leaved Pine *Pinus palustris* Pl. 5

This tree grows from 100 to 120 feet tall. The wood is hard, strong and coarse, much valued for lumber, turpentine and resin. The leaves are 8 to 18 inches long. The cones are 6 to 10 inches long.

Long-leaved Pine is found in wet ground mainly on the coastal plain from southern Virginia to Florida and westward as far as eastern Texas. Plate 7 shows a cluster of staminate cones. The specimen came from Ladies Island near Beaufort, South Carolina.

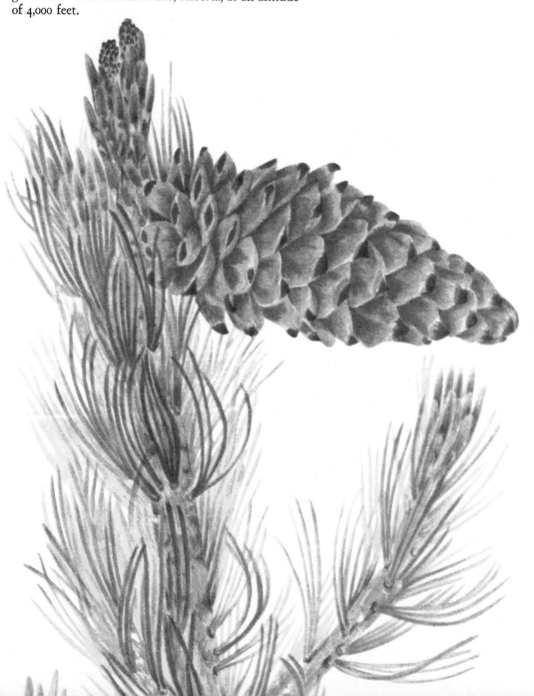

Western Red Cedar *Thuja plicata* Pl. 7.▶

Unfortunately the name Cedar has been given to several trees superficially alike but only distantly related botanically. Western Red Cedar is related to Arbor Vitae but is not in the same genus as Eastern Red Cedar; the latter is a species of *Juniperus*. Besides these, the White Cedar of the eastern states is still another genus. The true Cedars of the Old World are *Cedrus*. The name Western Red Cedar is applied also to another western species, *Juniperus occidentalis*. All of which demonstrates the unreliability of common names and the necessity for scientific nomenclature.

The leaves of *Thuja plicata* are scale-like, covering the branchlets in 4 rows. The cones are very small; the seed cones are only half an inch long when mature.

The tree grows to a height of 200 feet. The wood is light in weight and soft and is used in cabinet work and interior finish. Indians made much use of the wood for building canoes and lodges and of the fibrous bark for blankets and thatch.

It is found in the coastal ranges of Oregon and California, northward into British Columbia, and eastward to Idaho and Montana, from sea level to 7,000 feet.

◀Loblolly Pine *Pinus taeda* Pl. 6.

Loblolly Pine is a tall tree growing from 80 to 100 feet in height. The wood, although weak, is used commercially. The leaves of this species are short and stiff, 6 to 9 inches long. The cones are 2 to 6 inches long.

It is found in sandy soil and old fields from New Jersey to Florida and westward to western Louisiana and eastern Texas.

A cluster of staminate cones is shown in the figure. The specimen came from Beaufort, South Carolina.

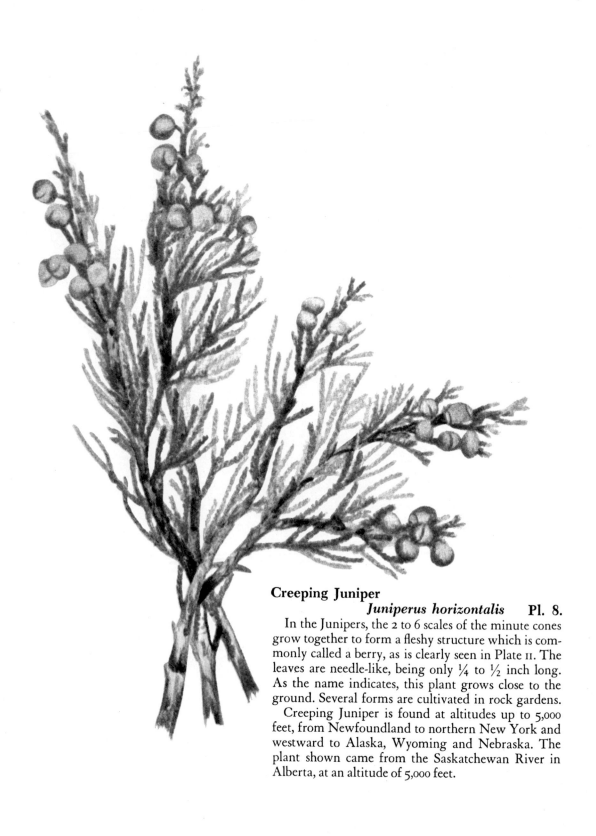

Creeping Juniper
Juniperus horizontalis   **Pl. 8.**

In the Junipers, the 2 to 6 scales of the minute cones grow together to form a fleshy structure which is commonly called a berry, as is clearly seen in Plate II. The leaves are needle-like, being only ¼ to ½ inch long. As the name indicates, this plant grows close to the ground. Several forms are cultivated in rock gardens.

Creeping Juniper is found at altitudes up to 5,000 feet, from Newfoundland to northern New York and westward to Alaska, Wyoming and Nebraska. The plant shown came from the Saskatchewan River in Alberta, at an altitude of 5,000 feet.

Flowering Plants. Angiospermae

This family contains the sedges, grass-like plants with inconspicuous greenish or brownish flowers. The stems are usually solid and triangular in cross section, and the leaf blades spring from sheaths which completely enclose the stem; whereas in the grasses the stem is often hollow and round, and the leaf sheath is open down one side.

The Arum family has numerous small flowers, sometimes lacking sepals and petals, closely packed on a stalk called the spadix, which is often thick and fleshy; around the spadix usually extends a sheathing leaf or spathe, often colored and mistaken for a petal. Most species of the family are tropical.

◀Arrowleaf *Sagittaria cuneata* Pl. 9.

On each flowering stalk the lower flowers are usually pistillate, the upper staminate. There are 3 sepals, 3 white petals, and many stamens and pistils in each flower. The pistils become small seed-like fruits crowded in a dense globular head. This species sometimes grows submerged, and then instead of arrow-shaped leaves, ribbon-like leaves are formed.

This Arrowleaf (there are several other species) grows in wet places from Nova Scotia and Quebec to New Jersey and westward to British Columbia, California and New Mexico. The specimen used for the painting came from Edgewater, British Columbia, at an altitude of 2,700 feet.

Golden Sedge *Carex aurea* Pl. 10.

The enormous genus *Carex* includes over 500 species in North America alone, and is abundant all over the world, chiefly in the cooler parts. The tiny flowers lack recognizable sepals and petals; they stand next to scales, in small clusters called spikelets; the stamens and pistils are in separate flowers, and these are often in different parts of the flower cluster. The pistils become small seed-like fruits, which are enveloped by a special covering. In the Golden Sedge this special envelope is golden brown, and, with the brownish-green scales, imparts a golden color to the oval spikelets.

Golden Sedge grows in wet places from Newfoundland to Connecticut and westward to British Columbia, California and New Mexico. The specimen illustrated was found in the valley of the Siffleur River, Alberta, at an altitude of 5,000 feet.

Jack-in-the-pulpit, Indian Turnip
Arisaema triphyllum   Pl. 11

"Jack" is the upper part of the spadix; the "pulpit" is the spathe. The flowers are on the lower part of the spadix; the pistillate flowers form the red berries which are visible when the spathe withers away.

The underground stem (corm) was eaten by the Indians *after being thoroughly boiled;* in the raw state it causes an intense burning sensation of the mouth, which lasts for a long time.

Jack-in-the-pulpit grows in woods and wet places from Nova Scotia to Florida, and westward to Minnesota and Louisiana. The plant used for illustration grew in Bryn Mawr, Pennsylvania.

Wild Calla *Calla palustris*   **Pl. 12.**

As in the familiar Calla Lily, the spathe of this plant is white and may be mistaken for a single petal. The true flowers, however, are the small objects which cover the entire surface of the spadix.

Wild Calla frequents cold bogs and shallow water from Newfoundland to Florida and westward to Alaska, Minnesota, Colorado and Texas. The illustration was made from a plant growing near Sudbury, Ontario.

Golden Club *Orontium aquaticum* Pl. 13.

The "golden club" is the spadix covered by the yellow flowers; it is not enveloped in the spathe, which in this species is merely a sheath around its stalk. Gnats and other small insects frequent the flowers.

Golden Club grows in swamps and shallow water from Massachusetts to Florida and westward to central New York, Kentucky and Louisiana. The plant shown grew in Beaufort, South Carolina.

Spiderwort *Tradescantia virginiana* Pl. 14.▶

Like those of the Lily Family, the flowers have parts mostly in threes and sixes. The 3 petals are blue, purple or rose, or occasionally white; they soon wither away. Below the flower-cluster is a pair of leaf-like bracts, usually unequal in length. The common name is derived from the narrow stiff leaves which project on all sides of the flower-cluster like so many legs.

A relative of this genus, often a creeping pest in gardens, is *Commelina,* the common Day Flower, whose 2 upper petals are sky-blue.

Spiderwort grows in prairies, roadsides and thickets from Maine to Georgia and westward to Minnesota, Missouri and Tennessee. The plant illustrated grew near Washington, D. C.

Pickerel Weed *Pontederia cordata* **Pl. 15.**

As the common name indicates, the plant grows in water, with the lustrous green leaves and spikes of pale blue or lavender flowers emerging from the surface. Each flower has a perianth of 6 parts, all much alike in color, the upper 3 joined to form an upper lip. There are 6 stamens. The ovary has 3 chambers, but only one forms a seed.

Pickerel Weed grows from Nova Scotia to Florida and westward to Minnesota and Texas. The plant shown in the painting came from Washington, D. C.

Pineapple family. Bromeliaceae Page 30

The Bromeliads are mostly air plants; that is, they grow attached to the branches of trees and have no direct connection with the ground. They are not parasites, for they do not obtain food from the supporting plant. Such a habit of life is limited to warm humid regions; air plants are most abundant in the tropics. Other members of the family are the pineapple and the Spanish Moss (not a moss but a flowering plant) which hangs from the trees so abundantly in our southern states.

Lily family. Liliaceae Page 31

The Lily Family supplies us with many familiar flowers — Lilies, Hyacinths, Tulips, Lilies-of-the-valley, Onions, Asparagus, and many others. All are characterized by flowers with a perianth of 6 segments (often in 2 sets of 3, but usually all colored alike), 6 stamens, and a 3-chambered ovary which is never wholly inferior. The fruit may be a pod or a berry. Many species grow from bulbs or underground stems; but a few, such as the Joshua Tree, are tree-like.

DOG-TOOTH VIOLET, ADDER'S-TONGUE *ERYTHRONIUM* Page 32

The flowering stem of these plants arises, with the pair of leaves which envelop it, from a bulb deep under the surface. The bulb may propagate itself by sending out slender runners at the tips of which new bulbs are formed. Plants which have not yet reached flowering age (which may require severals years) have only a single leaf. The nodding flowers, one or several on a stalk in a variety of colors, closely resemble small lilies; the fruit is a small 3-angled pod.

The name *Erythronium* is derived from a Greek word meaning red. The European species has a reddish-purple flower. The word violet was once applied to any spring flower. Adder's-tongue seems to allude to the mottled leaves of some species, which suggest snake-skin.

LILY *LILIUM* Page 35

The large genus *Lilium* needs little introduction. It grows in many parts of the world — Asia, Europe and North America. The plants are mostly tall and leafy, with large flowers of all shades of white, yellow, orange and red. The numerical pattern of the family is clearly seen in these flowers — 6 perianth parts all more or less alike in color, 6 stamens, and a 3-chambered ovary which becomes a 3-sided pod. The stigma is 3-lobed. The flower may have the form of a funnel, or the parts of the perianth may be reflexed as in the familiar Tiger-lily. The flowering stems arise from an underground scaly bulb or rootstock.

MARIPOSA LILY *CALOCHORTUS* Page 37

There are about 50 kinds of Mariposa Lilies, natives of western North America. The leaves and flowering stalks arise from small underground stems known as corms. There are only a few flowers to a plant, often only one. They have extraordinary variety and charm, ranging in color from white to blue, purple, yellow, orange, and even red. There are 3 broad concave petals, with a gland at the base which is frequently of a contrasting color and texture; 3 often narrow and variously colored sepals; 6 stamens; and the 3-chambered ovary characteristic of the family, which becomes a small pod. The generic name is derived from two Greek words meaning beautiful grass.

TRILLIUM, WAKE ROBIN *TRILLIUM* Page 42

The Trilliums have not only their flower parts in threes but their leaves also: there are 3 leaves just beneath the single flower. Furthermore, these leaves differ from most leaves of the Lily Family and related families in being net-veined instead of parallel-veined. The flowers also differ from most liliaceous flowers in having 3 green sepals contrasting with 3 colored petals. The stem arises from a short tuber underground. These plants are spring-flowering inhabitants of rich woods.

Tillandsia *Tillandsia fasciculata* Pl. 16.

This Tillandsia (there are over 100 species of the genus) may be distinguished from others by the long rigid leaves with their edges inrolled. It has narrow blue flowers in a spike covered with red-tinged scales (bracts).

It grows in southern Florida, and in the West Indies and Central America. The plant illustrated was found in a hammock near West Palm Beach, Florida.

Camass *Camassia quamash* Pl. 17.

Several kinds of Camass are common in moist meadows of the Pacific states and the Rocky Mountains, and one in open woodlands of the Midwest. *Camassia quamash* is distinguished by the deep blue color and the slight irregularity of the perianth: 5 of the perianth parts grow upward, leaving the lowermost extending downward by itself. The ovary supports a single style. The plant reaches a height of 2 feet. The bulbs were valued as food by the Indians, who gave them the name "quamash."

This Camass grows from Montana and Utah to British Columbia and southward along the Coast Ranges to California. The plant sketched was found in Glacier National Park, Montana.

White Adder's-tongue, Dog-tooth
Violet   *Erythronium albidum*   Pl. 18

This is the common species of the Midwest, grow-ing in meadows and open woodlands, often in rocky soil. Its flowers are solitary, and vary in color from cream-white to bluish. The style is 3-cleft at the tip, with 3 stigmas. The leaves are usually, but not always, mottled.

White Adder's-tongue grows from southern On-tario to Georgia and westward to Minnesota, Mis-souri and Oklahoma. The plant illustrated was found in the Potomac Valley.

Yellow Adder's-tongue, Dog-tooth Violet   *Erythronium americanum*   Pl. 19.

Yellow Adder's-tongue is common in the Atlantic states, growing in the rich loam of open woods. The flowers are solitary. The stamens may be of 2 sizes, 3 of each size, and they vary in color in different races. The style is not cleft and the one stigma is 3-lobed. The leaves are mottled.

Erythronium americanum is found from Nova Scotia to Florida and westward to Minnesota and Oklahoma (becoming scarcer as one goes westward). The painting was made near Washington, D. C.

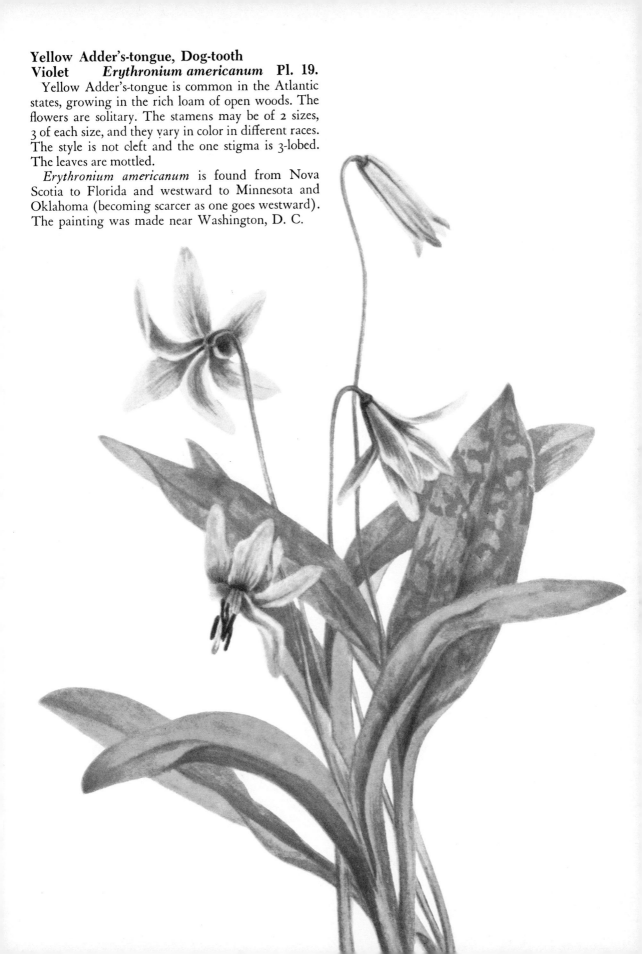

Avalanche Lily

Erythronium montanum **Pl. 20.**

Avalanche Lily grows on high mountain slopes, often appearing at the edge of the melting snow in spring or even growing up through the snow. There may be several flowers on a stalk. The stigma is 3-parted. The leaves are green, not mottled.

Erythronium montanum is found only in Washington and Oregon. The plant sketched grew in Paradise Valley on the slopes of Mount Rainier, Washington.

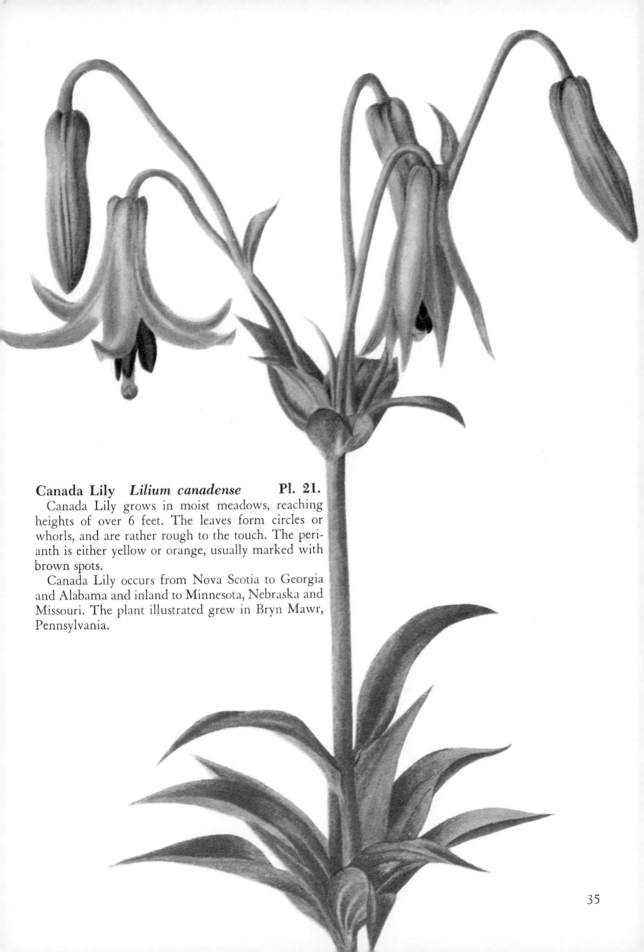

Canada Lily *Lilium canadense* Pl. 21.

Canada Lily grows in moist meadows, reaching heights of over 6 feet. The leaves form circles or whorls, and are rather rough to the touch. The perianth is either yellow or orange, usually marked with brown spots.

Canada Lily occurs from Nova Scotia to Georgia and Alabama and inland to Minnesota, Nebraska and Missouri. The plant illustrated grew in Bryn Mawr, Pennsylvania.

Western Red Lily
Lilium umbellatum Pl. 22.

The Western Red Lily is a close relative of the Wood Lily of the eastern states, *Lilium philadelphicum,* and is sometimes classified as a variety of that species. Both are distinguished by their brilliant color and by having their perianth parts tapering at the base to narrow claws. *Lilium umbellatum* grows about 3 feet high. Its leaves are scattered and rather narrow (those of *Lilium philadelphicum* are broader and form whorls).

Lilium umbellatum grows in wet meadows from Ontario to British Columbia and southward to Ohio, and along the Rocky Mountains to New Mexico. The painting was made near Radium Hot Springs, British Columbia, at an altitude of 3,000 feet.

Lilac Mariposa
Calochortus splendens **Pl. 23.**

The stems of the Lilac Mariposa are branched, with a flower at the end of each branch. Long tangled hairs grow sparsely from the lilac or purple petals. The pod is narrow and may be over 2 inches long.

The species is found on dry stony hills, often in the low brush called chaparral, in the coast ranges of southern California. The plant illustrated grew at Santa Ana.

37

Golden Bowl *Calochortus clavatus* **Pl. 24.**

The stem is zigzag, branched, and up to 3 feet tall, with the flowers in a cluster. The sepals are rather broad and yellowish; the yellow petals bear hairs which are club-shaped. The 3-inch pod is long-pointed.

Golden Bowl grows on wooded slopes in southern California.

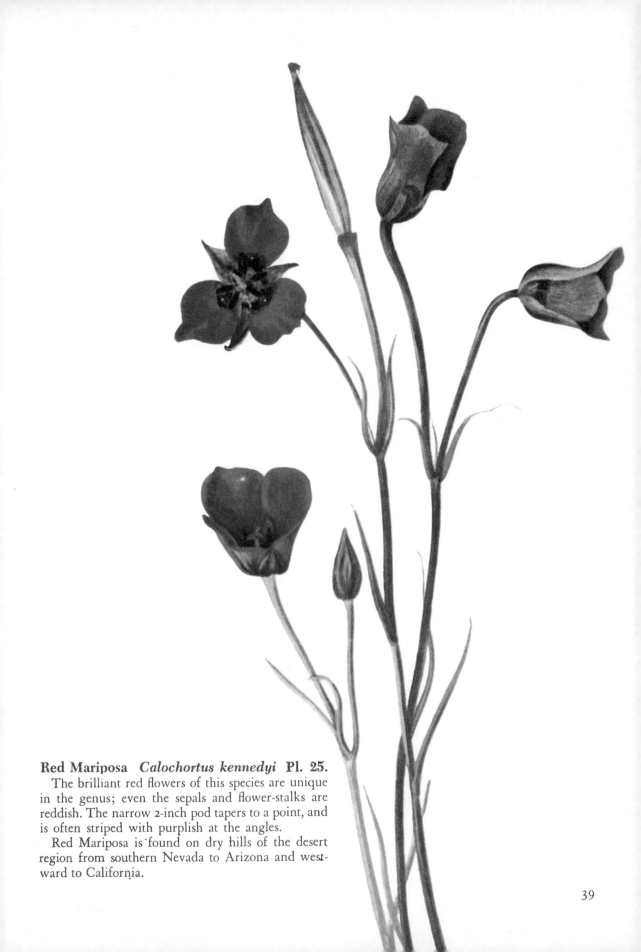

Red Mariposa *Calochortus kennedyi* **Pl. 25.**

The brilliant red flowers of this species are unique
in the genus; even the sepals and flower-stalks are
reddish. The narrow 2-inch pod tapers to a point, and
is often striped with purplish at the angles.

Red Mariposa is found on dry hills of the desert
region from southern Nevada to Arizona and westward to California.

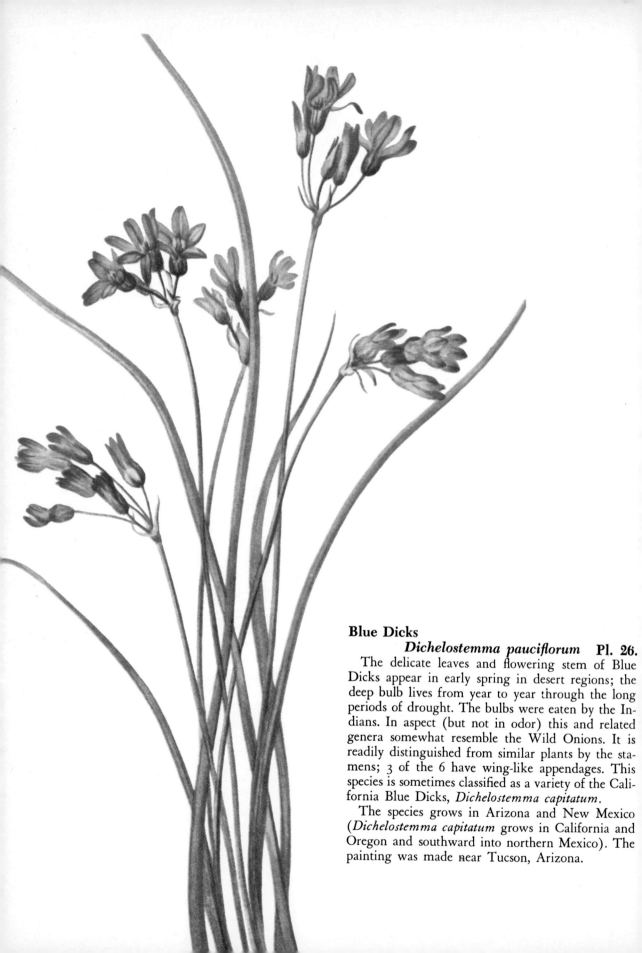

Blue Dicks

Dichelostemma pauciflorum **Pl. 26.**

The delicate leaves and flowering stem of Blue Dicks appear in early spring in desert regions; the deep bulb lives from year to year through the long periods of drought. The bulbs were eaten by the Indians. In aspect (but not in odor) this and related genera somewhat resemble the Wild Onions. It is readily distinguished from similar plants by the stamens; 3 of the 6 have wing-like appendages. This species is sometimes classified as a variety of the California Blue Dicks, *Dichelostemma capitatum*.

The species grows in Arizona and New Mexico (*Dichelostemma capitatum* grows in California and Oregon and southward into northern Mexico). The painting was made near Tucson, Arizona.

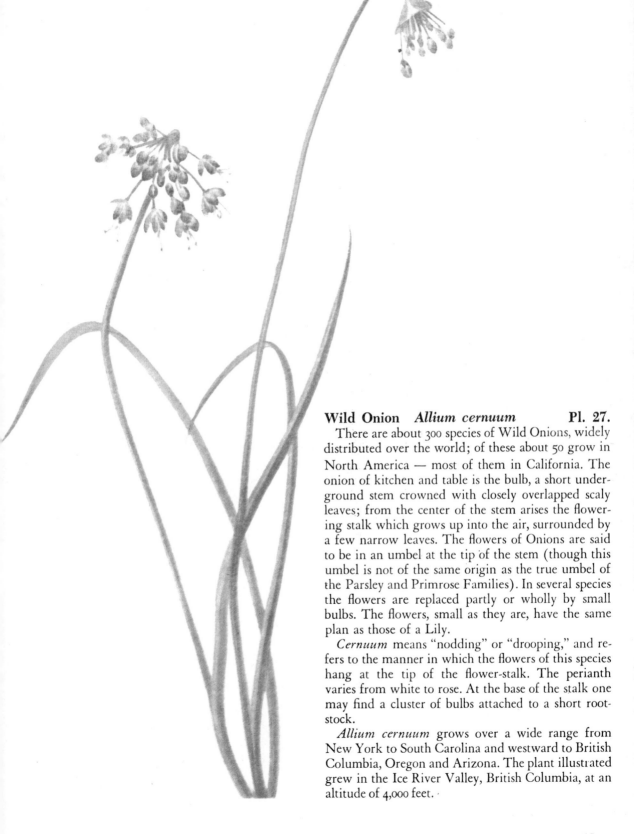

Wild Onion   *Allium cernuum*   Pl. 27.

There are about 300 species of Wild Onions, widely distributed over the world; of these about 50 grow in North America — most of them in California. The onion of kitchen and table is the bulb, a short underground stem crowned with closely overlapped scaly leaves; from the center of the stem arises the flowering stalk which grows up into the air, surrounded by a few narrow leaves. The flowers of Onions are said to be in an umbel at the tip of the stem (though this umbel is not of the same origin as the true umbel of the Parsley and Primrose Families). In several species the flowers are replaced partly or wholly by small bulbs. The flowers, small as they are, have the same plan as those of a Lily.

Cernuum means "nodding" or "drooping," and refers to the manner in which the flowers of this species hang at the tip of the flower-stalk. The perianth varies from white to rose. At the base of the stalk one may find a cluster of bulbs attached to a short rootstock.

Allium cernuum grows over a wide range from New York to South Carolina and westward to British Columbia, Oregon and Arizona. The plant illustrated grew in the Ice River Valley, British Columbia, at an altitude of 4,000 feet.

Purple Trillium *Trillium erectum* **Pl. 28, 29.**
    The leaves are very broad with a short sharp point. The petals vary in color from brown-purple to pink, white or greenish. There are 3 distinct spreading stigmas. The scent of the flowers is unpleasant, for which reason it is sometimes called Stinking Benjamin. The pod is winged on the angles.
    Plate 29 shows the white-flowered form of this species, sometimes classified as a distinct species under the name *Trillium album.*
    Trillium erectum grows from Quebec to Georgia (in the mountains) and westward to Ontario and Tennessee. The specimen shown in Plate 28 was collected at Washington, D. C. The white-flowered form came from near Chestnut Hill, Massachusetts.

PLATE 29

Trillium *Trillium grandiflorum* **Pl. 30.**

The petals of this species are unusually broad, at first white then turning rose-pink, or marked with green. The 3 stigmas are narrow but stand erect. The pod is almost globular, winged on the angles. There is a pink-flowered form in cultivation.

Trillium grandiflorum grows from Quebec to Georgia and westward to Minnesota and Missouri. The specimen illustrated came from Washington, D. C.

Painted Trillium
Trillium undulatum Pl. 31.

This is the showiest of our Trilliums. The common name refers to the petals, with their red or purplish markings at the base. The leaves taper to their points. The pod is not winged, and rather broad.

Painted Trillium grows from Nova Scotia to Georgia (in the mountains) and westward to Wisconsin and Missouri. The specimen illustrated came from eastern Massachusetts.

Giant Trillium
Trillium chloropetalum Pl. 32.

The Giant Trillium grows to a height of nearly 2 feet. It has almost round leaves, which are usually mottled. The flower is sessile like that of *Trillium sessile*. The petals are maroon or greenish-yellow or even white. The first form discovered, from which the species was named, was the greenish-flowered form; *chloropetalum* means "with green petals." The fruit is conspicuously winged.

Giant Trillium ranges from Washington to California. The specimen from which the painting was made was cultivated in Boston, Massachusetts.

Amaryllis family. Amaryllidaceae Page 48

Iris family. Iridaceae Page 49

The Iris Family includes several kinds of plants that at first sight do not suggest the Iris: Gladiolus, Freesia, Sisyrinchium. Some members of the family have irregular flowers, in which the upper parts differ from the lower in shape, size, and sometimes color; others, like the Iris itself and Blue-eyed Grass, have a regular perianth, radially symmetrical. The Iris Family resembles the Amaryllis Family in having an inferior ovary; it differs from it in having 3 stamens instead of 6.

IRIS   *IRIS* Page 50

The flowers of Iris are well known and sufficiently identify the genus. The 6-parted perianth consists of 3 outer, erect parts: the standards; and 3 inner, reflexed parts: the falls; both of these sets have a wide variety of colors and markings. There are 3 stamens, projecting over the 3 falls. And the 3 branches of the style resemble petals in texture and color; they extend over the stamens, carrying the stigmas on their lower surface. The ovary, as in all members of the family, is inferior.

The leaves, which arise from an underground stem or tuber, are curiously folded, each embracing the next younger. Linnaeus described this arrangement fancifully as equitant, i.e., after the manner of a rider bestriding a horse. This peculiar feature is found also in other members of the family.

48

Blue-eyed Grass
Sisyrinchium angustifolium Pl. 34.

Like Star Grass, this plant owes its English name to it narrow grass-like leaves; members of the Grass Family do not have a colored perianth. The leaves of Blue-eyed Grass are like those of Iris in arrangement. Two small membranous scales which are folded around the bases of the flower-stalks in this genus form a spathe (compare the Araceae, in which family the spathe consists of one leaf). The inferior ovary becomes a small brown globular pod.

Sisyrinchium angustifolium grows in fields and wet sandy soil from Newfoundland to Virginia, westward to British Columbia, and southward in the Rocky Mountains. The plants illustrated were found in the valley of the Ghost River near Banff, Alberta, at an altitude of 4,000 feet.

◀**Star Grass** *Hypoxis hirsuta* Pl. 33.

The yellow perianth marks this plant as not a true grass, in spite of its narrow leaves. The leaves overtop the flower-stalk, which bears usually several small 6-parted flowers with inferior ovaries (usually only one in bloom at a time). The perianth is greenish outside and hairy.

Star Grass grows in meadows and open woodlands from Maine to Florida and westward to Manitoba, Kansas and Texas.

Dwarf Iris *Iris verna*   **Pl. 36.**

This Iris is recognized by its low stature (only 6 inches high) and grass-like leaves. The falls and standards are about equal in length. There is no crest or beard on the falls. The pod is blunt on the angles.

Dwarf Iris is found on wooded hillsides from Pennsylvania to Florida and westward to Kentucky and Mississippi, mostly on sandy soil. The painting was made near Beaufort, South Carolina.

◀**Large Blue Flag** *Iris versicolor*   **Pl. 35.**

The Large Blue Flag has standards considerably longer than the falls. The falls lack the crest or beard which are found in other species (e.g., the common garden Bearded Iris).

Iris versicolor grows in wet places from Labrador and Newfoundland to Virginia and westward to Manitoba and Minnesota. The plant illustrated was found near Washington, D. C.

Crested Dwarf Iris *Iris cristata* Pl. 37.

The crest which gives this Iris its name is the crinkled projection on the upper side of the falls. The flowers are sweet-smelling. The leaves are broader, less grass-like, than those of *Iris verna*. The pod is sharply triangular in section.

Iris cristata grows in rich woods from Maryland to Georgia and westward to Indiana and Missouri. The plants shown in the painting were found on Plummer's Island in the Potomac River near Washington, D. C.

Orchid family. Orchidaceae

The Orchids are usually associated with wealth and luxury; yet many species grow wild in our fields and forests. The largest and most gorgeous kinds are tropical; but even the smallest and least conspicuous share the complex flower structure which characterizes the family. The flower has 3 sepals and 3 petals. Of the petals, one, usually the lowermost, is different from the others in size, shape or color — or all three; this is called the lip. There is a single stamen in most of our orchids; 2 in the Lady's-slipper; and the stamen or stamens are united with the style and stigma to form a complex structure called the column, which occupies the center of the flower. At the summit of the column the pollen is more or less exposed, cohering in small masses called pollinia, and variously provided with an elaborate mechanism which affixes it to the bodies of visiting insects. Below the pollen is the large stigmatic surface. The ovary is inferior, and has 1 or 3 chambers. The ovary, with the surrounding tissues of the stem in which it is immersed, becomes a pod, usually 3-angled. The seeds are minute and very numerous.

Most of the tropical Orchids grow as epiphytes — not parasites — upon the trunks of trees. Epiphytes merely use other plants as supports, having themselves no direct connection with the ground; parasites, like Dodder and Mistletoe, obtain their nourishment from the host plant. Many of the epiphytic species bear pseudobulbs — large swollen branches which are reservoirs of food and water; their aerial roots are able to take water from the humid air. Our species often grow in boggy or acid soil, rich in organic matter, where their roots are associated with certain fungi — on which they are perhaps parasitic or partly so. Such complex relationships make it extremely difficult to transplant Orchids and cultivate them in ordinary gardens.

LADY'S-SLIPPER *CYPRIPEDIUM* Page 54

The name Lady's-slipper or Moccasin-flower refers to the large lip. Pollination is effected by bees and other insects, which enter the lip by the opening in its upper side and feed on the nectar inside; to escape they must crawl out past the column, taking with them some of the sticky pollen-masses; these may come in contact with the stigma of the next flower visited.

In most species of this genus the 2 lower sepals are united so that there appear to be only 2 in all.

REIN-ORCHIS, FRINGED ORCHIS *HABENARIA* Page 57

Habenaria is a large genus of about 500 species which grow in woodlands, meadows and swamps all over the world; at least 39 species occur in North America. There are usually many small flowers closely arranged on one flowering stem. The uppermost sepal forms a hood over the column; the 2 lateral petals adhere to this; the other sepals extend outward. The lip is prolonged backward into a hollow spur, in which nectar collects.

LADIES' TRESSES *SPIRANTHES* Page 61

The genus *Spiranthes* contains 300 species of orchids. They bear a flowering stem on which the small flowers are closely packed usually in a spiral (whence the name). The flowers are usually white or greenish, in some species red or orange or lavender. The upper sepal adheres to the lateral petals to form a small hood over the column. The genus is known in tropical Asia, Australia and New Zealand as well as in Europe and North and South America.

◀Ram's-head Lady's-slipper
Cypripedium arietinum   Pl. 38.

This is the only North American Lady's-slipper in which the 3 sepals are all distinct. The sepals and the lateral petals are greenish-brown; the lip is streaked white and red. The lip, only half an inch long, has a conical projection below. The species is easily distinguished also by its slender stature and narrow, lance-shaped leaves. A single flower grows at the summit of the stem.

Ram's-head Lady's-slipper grows from Quebec to New York and westward to Manitoba, Wisconsin and Illinois. It occurs also in China. The plant illustrated grew in Chittenden County, Vermont.

Showy Orchis   Orchis spectabilis   Pl. 39.

The Showy Orchis forms but 2 leaves, broad and glossy and sheathing the base of the flowering stem. The flowers rarely rise to a height of more than a foot above the ground. The sepals and lateral petals come together over the column to form a sort of hood, usually rose-pink or lilac in color, sometimes even purple, rarely almost white. The lip is white, and extends backward beside the flower-stalk in a tubular spur, in which nectar collects.

It is found from New Brunswick and Quebec to Georgia and westward to Minnesota, Nebraska, Kansas and Arkansas. The painting was made near Washington, D. C.

Round-leaved Orchis
Orchis rotundifolia Pl. 40.

As the painting shows, the plant forms a single leaf close to the ground. The flowering stem grows to a height of about a foot, bearing as many as 16 flowers. Like the preceding species, the lateral petals and sepals, which vary from white to pink or mauve, form a hood over the column. The lip is white, spotted with magenta-pink or purplish, and is 3-lobed.

Charles Darwin conducted his celebrated experiments upon pollination with European species of this genus.

The Round-leaved Orchis grows from Greenland to New York and westward to Alaska, British Columbia and Wyoming. The plants shown were found near Field, British Columbia, at an altitude of 3,800 feet.

Orange-plume *Habenaria ciliaris*   Pl. 41.

The stem of this species may grow to a height of more than 3 feet; it bears a number of lance-shaped, rather rigid leaves. The lip is copiously fringed to a length of nearly half an inch *(ciliaris* means "provided with cilia" or eyelashes, and refers to this fringe).

Orange-plume is found from Ontario to Florida and westward to Wisconsin, Missouri and Texas. The plant illustrated grew near Bridgeport, Connecticut.

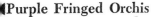
Purple Fringed Orchis

Habenaria psycodes **Pl. 42.**

This species has a stem sometimes over 3 feet high, which bears several large sheathing leaves. The flowers vary in color from almost white to pinkish or lavender. The lip is deeply cleft in 3 parts, the lateral divisions themselves cleft, and all the margin deeply fringed (*psycodes* means "butterfly-like"). The flowers vary greatly also in size; plants with large flowers (the lip ¾ inch long) have sometimes been classified as a variety or even as a distinct species, *Habenaria grandiflora*.

Purple Fringed Orchis grows from Newfoundland to Georgia and westward to Minnesota, Iowa and Kentucky. The painting was made on Mount Desert Island, Maine.

Rose Pogonia

Pogonia ophioglossoides **Pl. 43.**

This graceful orchid usually has but one leaf and one flower; but, as in the painting, some plants (especially those of the south) have 2 or 3 flowers, with a corresponding number of leaves. The stem grows as much as 2 feet high. The flowers vary in color from white to rose, all the segments of the perianth being of much the same shade. The lip is abundantly fringed, and bears a beard of yellowish hairs near its center. The flowers are said to have the fragrance of fresh raspberries.

Rose Pogonia is fairly common in bogs from Newfoundland and Quebec to Florida and westward to Minnesota, Missouri and Texas. The plants shown were found near Tuckerton, New Jersey.

59

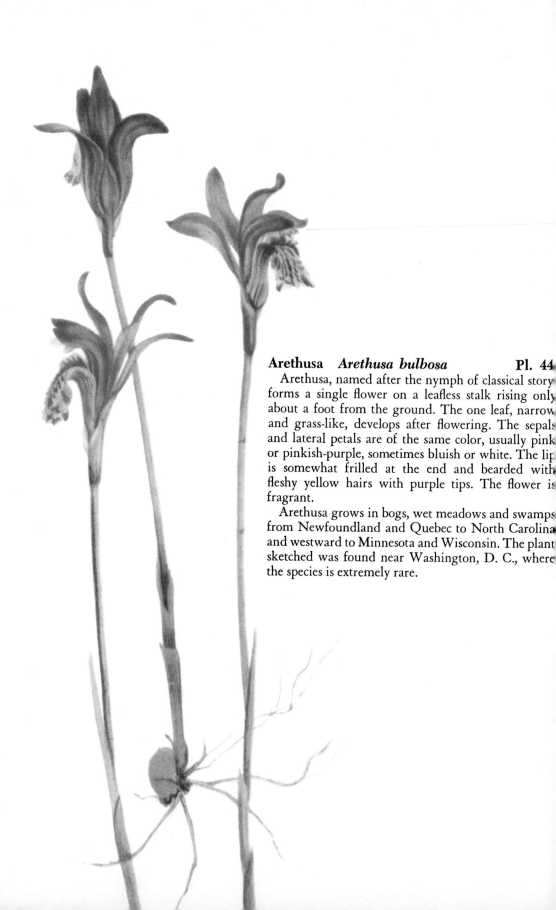

Arethusa   *Arethusa bulbosa*   Pl. 44

Arethusa, named after the nymph of classical story, forms a single flower on a leafless stalk rising only about a foot from the ground. The one leaf, narrow and grass-like, develops after flowering. The sepals and lateral petals are of the same color, usually pink or pinkish-purple, sometimes bluish or white. The lip is somewhat frilled at the end and bearded with fleshy yellow hairs with purple tips. The flower is fragrant.

Arethusa grows in bogs, wet meadows and swamps from Newfoundland and Quebec to North Carolina and westward to Minnesota and Wisconsin. The plant sketched was found near Washington, D. C., where the species is extremely rare.

Butterfly Orchid
Epidendrum tampense Pl. 45.

The genus *Epidendrum* is mostly tropical; there are about 800 species scattered through Mexico, Central and South America and the West Indies. Most of the species grow attached to trees *(Epidendrum* is from two Greek words meaning "upon a tree"). Several species grow in Florida. The yellowish sepals and lateral petals are alike in color, and contrast with the pink-striped lip, which is 3-lobed.

This is the most abundant epiphytic orchid in Florida. It occurs also in Cuba and the Bahama Islands.

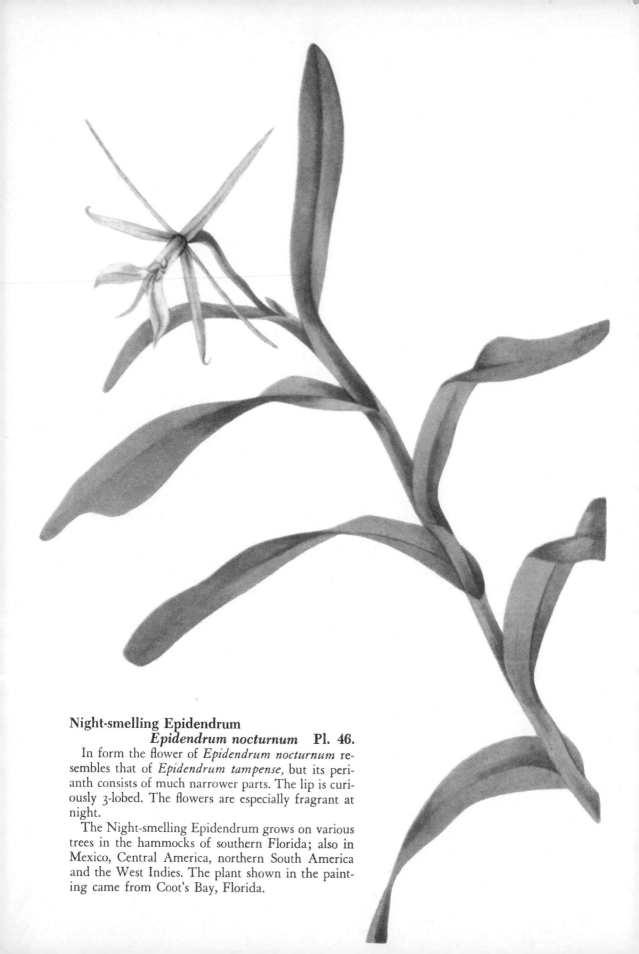

Night-smelling Epidendrum
Epidendrum nocturnum Pl. 46.

In form the flower of *Epidendrum nocturnum* resembles that of *Epidendrum tampense,* but its perianth consists of much narrower parts. The lip is curiously 3-lobed. The flowers are especially fragrant at night.

The Night-smelling Epidendrum grows on various trees in the hammocks of southern Florida; also in Mexico, Central America, northern South America and the West Indies. The plant shown in the painting came from Coot's Bay, Florida.

Bee-swarm or Cowhorn Orchid
Cyrtopodium punctatum Pl. 47.

The Bee-swarm Orchid answers the popular concept of an orchid better than most North American species of the family. It is a large epiphytic species, often over 3 feet tall. The leaves and flower stalks grow from pseudobulbs which are sometimes over a foot long (the "cowhorns"). The lateral petals and the sepals are much alike in form and color. The lip is joined with the base of the column; it is 3-lobed and thick and warty in the middle.

The Bee-swarm Orchid is found on tree trunks or rotten logs in hammocks and cypress swamps of southern Florida; also in Mexico, Central and South America, and the West Indies. It has long been known in cultivation. The plant shown in the painting was collected at Coot's Bay, Florida.

Pussy Willow   *Salix discolor*   Pl. 48.

The genus *Salix* includes some 300 species which grow mostly in the north temperate zone, frequently along streams or in swamps. More than 100 are found in North America. The species are often difficult to distinguish, and matters are complicated by the fact that many species hybridize in nature. Staminate and pistillate flowers are borne on different plants, in pendent clusters known as catkins. They have no perianth. Each staminate flower consists only of a few stamens (from 1 to 7); each pistillate flower consists of a single pistil. A small scale grows underneath each flower; there is also a small gland (or sometimes 2) at the base of stamens or pistil. In some species the catkins appear before the leaves, in others at the same time. The gray silky hairs that appear early in spring on branches of Pussy Willow are attached to the scales of the catkins. As they lengthen, the 2 stamens or the single pistil of each flower become evident.

Pussy Willow grows from Newfoundland to Delaware and westward to British Columbia and Missouri. The illustration was made from a plant growing in Washington, D. C.

Drummond's Willow
Salix drummondiana Pl. 49.

This is a species of the high mountains. The leaves are whitened on the under surface with fine curled hairs. There are 2 stamens in each staminate flower. The illustration shows the capsules open and liberating the seeds; the fine hairs grow from the seed-coats, enabling the wind to carry the seeds long distances.

Drummond's Willow grows in the Rocky Mountains in Alberta and British Columbia. The painting was made on Sheep Creek, Alberta, at an elevation of 6,000 feet.

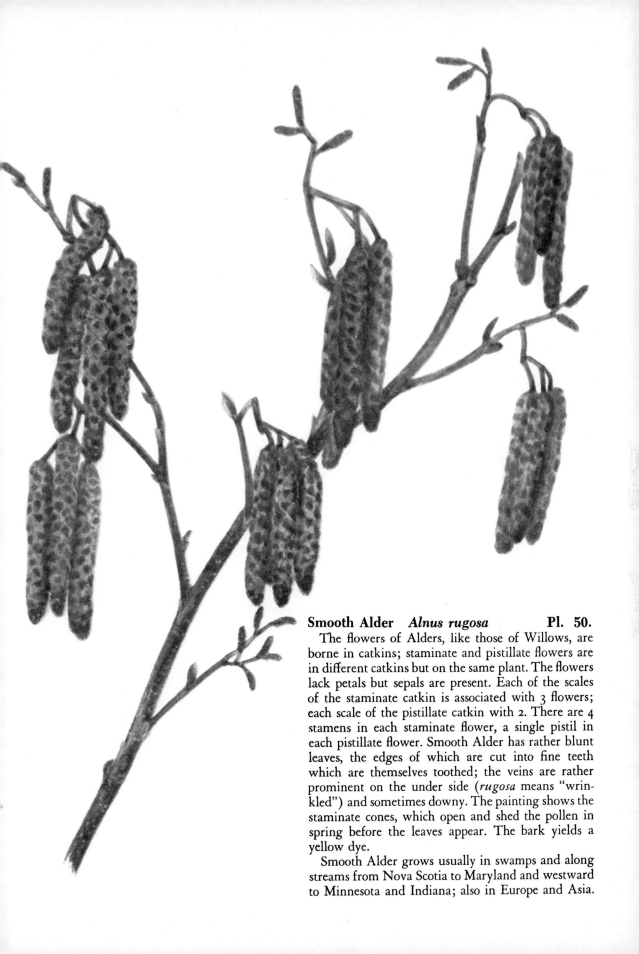

Smooth Alder *Alnus rugosa* **Pl. 50.**

The flowers of Alders, like those of Willows, are borne in catkins; staminate and pistillate flowers are in different catkins but on the same plant. The flowers lack petals but sepals are present. Each of the scales of the staminate catkin is associated with 3 flowers; each scale of the pistillate catkin with 2. There are 4 stamens in each staminate flower, a single pistil in each pistillate flower. Smooth Alder has rather blunt leaves, the edges of which are cut into fine teeth which are themselves toothed; the veins are rather prominent on the under side (*rugosa* means "wrinkled") and sometimes downy. The painting shows the staminate cones, which open and shed the pollen in spring before the leaves appear. The bark yields a yellow dye.

Smooth Alder grows usually in swamps and along streams from Nova Scotia to Maryland and westward to Minnesota and Indiana; also in Europe and Asia.

Mountain Alder   *Alnus sinuata*   Pl. 51.

The pistillate catkins of Alder, as they mature and form their small nuts, become woody cones. The illustration of Mountain Alder shows the condition in the autumn, when the pistillate cones of the previous spring are mature and woody, and the staminate cones which will open the following spring are already present. This is a shrub with sharp leaves, round at the base, smooth, sharply double-toothed and cut.

The staminate catkins may be 3 inches long; the pistillate catkins are less than an inch long in the spring when pollination occurs.

Mountain Alder grows along streams from Wyoming to British Columbia and southward in the Cascade Mountains to Oregon. The illustration was made near Glacier, British Columbia, at an altitude of 3,500 feet.

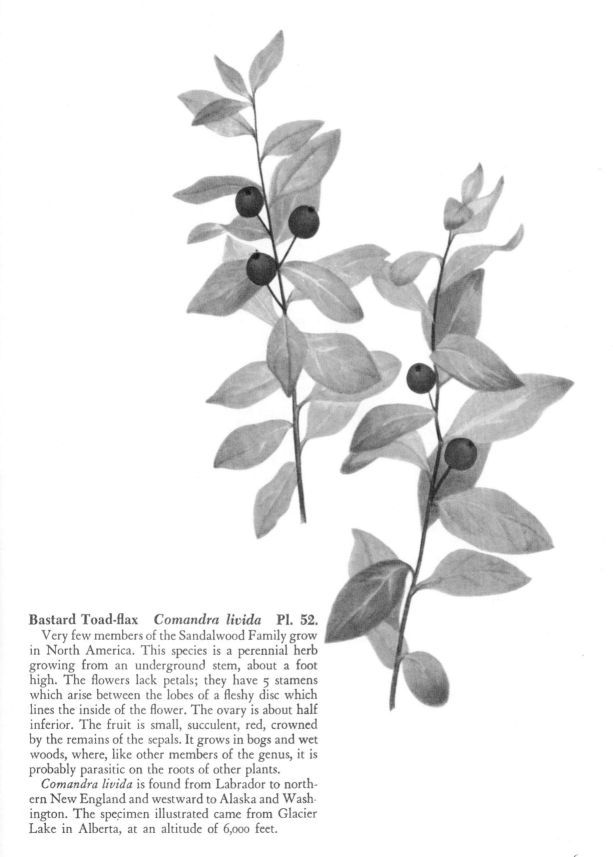

Bastard Toad-flax   *Comandra livida*   **Pl. 52.**

Very few members of the Sandalwood Family grow in North America. This species is a perennial herb growing from an underground stem, about a foot high. The flowers lack petals; they have 5 stamens which arise between the lobes of a fleshy disc which lines the inside of the flower. The ovary is about half inferior. The fruit is small, succulent, red, crowned by the remains of the sepals. It grows in bogs and wet woods, where, like other members of the genus, it is probably parasitic on the roots of other plants.

Comandra livida is found from Labrador to northern New England and westward to Alaska and Washington. The specimen illustrated came from Glacier Lake in Alberta, at an altitude of 6,000 feet.

Mistletoe *Phoradendron flavescens* Pl. 53.

Mistletoe is a true parasite, which sends suckers into the host tree and obtains food from it. Its greenish flowers have sepals but no petals. The stamens and pistils are found on different plants. The staminate flower has its sepals joined into a 3-lobed cup, and 3 stamens. The ovary is inferior and becomes the white berry.

This is not the common mistletoe of Europe, which is *Viscum album;* but both are placed in the same family. There are about 100 species of *Phoradendron,* all American and mostly tropical. Another large genus in this family is *Loranthus,* whose flowers are sometimes very showy.

Mistletoe grows from New Jersey to Florida and westward to Missouri and New Mexico. The specimen illustrated grew in Virginia.

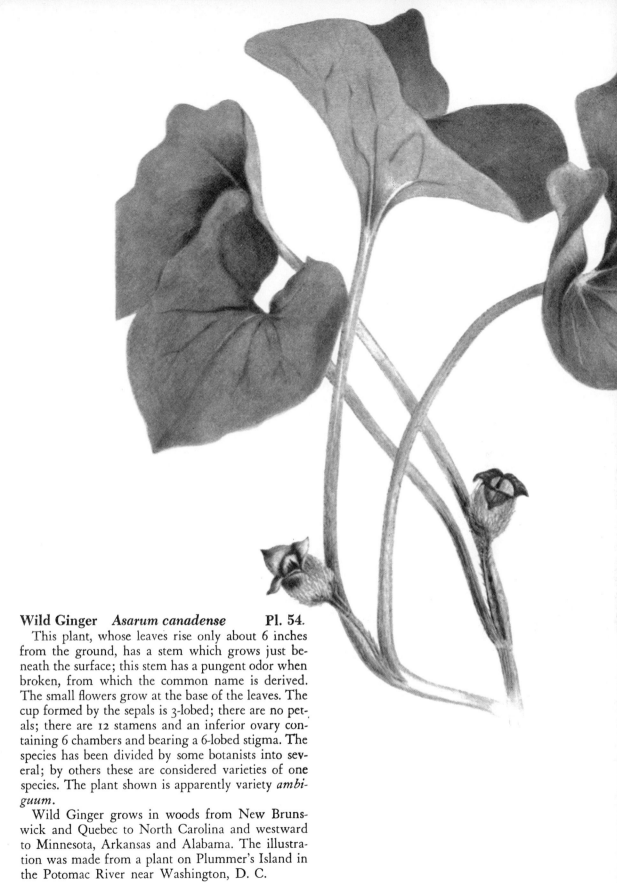

Wild Ginger   *Asarum canadense*   Pl. 54.

This plant, whose leaves rise only about 6 inches from the ground, has a stem which grows just beneath the surface; this stem has a pungent odor when broken, from which the common name is derived. The small flowers grow at the base of the leaves. The cup formed by the sepals is 3-lobed; there are no petals; there are 12 stamens and an inferior ovary containing 6 chambers and bearing a 6-lobed stigma. The species has been divided by some botanists into several; by others these are considered varieties of one species. The plant shown is apparently variety *ambiguum*.

Wild Ginger grows in woods from New Brunswick and Quebec to North Carolina and westward to Minnesota, Arkansas and Alabama. The illustration was made from a plant on Plummer's Island in the Potomac River near Washington, D. C.

Strawberry Blite
Chenopodium capitatum **Pl. 55.**

Many species of *Chenopodium* are weeds in gardens; the commonest is generally known as Lamb's Quarters. The flowers in this genus are small and greenish, with sepals but no petals, usually 5 stamens and an ovary bearing 2 or 3 styles. Some species are eaten as greens. Spinach and Beet are also members of the family. Strawberry Blite is easily known by the enlarged sepals which become fleshy and red as the fruit within them develops. The fruit itself is a small bladder containing a single seed.

Strawberry Blite grows in open places from Quebec to New Jersey westward to Alaska, and southward in the Rocky Mountains. The plant shown was found in Bow Valley, Alberta, at an altitude of 4,000 feet.

Nodding Campion   *Lychnis apetala*   Pl. 56.

This curious alpine plant has a much inflated sac formed from the joined sepals, which lasts until the fruit is formed within it. In spite of the name *(apetala* means "without petals") petals are present, but they are small and scarcely protrude from the sepal tube.

Nodding Campion is found from Greenland to Alaska and southward to Labrador, Montana, Colorado and Utah; also in Europe and Asia. The painting was made from a plant near Lake McArthur, British Columbia, at an altitude of 7,000 feet.

Moss Campion   *Silene acaulis*   Pl. 57.

This is an alpine species, growing in dense tussocks which rise only a few inches from the ground. Each stem is terminated by a single flower. The petals are pink, lilac or white. The capsule is partly divided into three chambers. The plant somewhat resembles the well-known Moss Pink, which is a species of Phlox, but differs in having the petals not united.

Moss Campion grows in the Arctic regions and southward to Nova Scotia, New Hampshire and Alaska and in the mountains to Arizona and Washington; also in Europe and Asia. The plant shown in the painting grew near Lake Louise in Alberta, at an altitude of 7,500 feet.

Naiad Spring Beauty
Montia parvifolia   Pl. 58.

Montia is a close relative of *Claytonia*. Its leaves are partly paired but many are scattered singly along the stems. The flowers are like those of Spring Beauty, but there are 3 distinct styles. The plant grows from an underground stem.

Naiad Spring Beauty occurs on the banks of streams from Alaska to California. The plant shown in the painting was found near Glacier House in the Selkirk Mountains of British Columbia, at an altitude of 3,500 feet.

Water-lily family. Nymphaeaceae Page 76

Buttercup family. Ranunculaceae Page 77

The Buttercup Family contains a large number of familiar plants — Buttercup, Anemone, Peony, Clematis, Columbine, Larkspur, and others. They are all herbaceous genera (i.e., not woody). The flower parts are mostly numerous and all separate. This applies even to the pistils, which are simple, each 1-chambered, each developing separately into a pod, a berry or a small nut-like 1-seeded fruit. Petals may be lacking and the sepals brightly colored instead. The family is relatively primitive, for the earliest flowering plants are thought to have had numerous distinct parts.

Magnolia family. Magnoliaceae Page 86

Of all the flowering plants of the present day, the Magnolias seem to come closest to the form which we suppose to have characterized the ancestors of the entire group. They are all woody, mostly tall trees. The flowers are borne singly at the ends of the branches. Flower parts are mostly numerous and to a certain extent are formed in a spiral (rather than in rings, cycles) upon a rather elongated central projection known as the receptacle. The pistils become 1- or 2-seeded pods. There are about 35 species of *Magnolia* in America and Asia, and many hybrids.

Custard-apple family. Annonaceae Page 87

Barberry family. Berberidaceae Page 88

Fumitory family. Fumariaceae Page 90

Water-lily *Nymphaea odorata* Pl. 59.
The stem of the Water-lily grows on the bottom of a pool or slow stream, rooting in the mud. The long leaf-stalks and the flower-stalks are attached to this underwater stem; they are pierced by channels filled with gases which thus circulate beneath the surface of the water. There are 4 sepals and many petals; the latter pass gradually into stamens through intermediate bodies (illustrating the commonly held botanical theory that petals are transformed stamens). The pistil is large and composed of many segments; each segment bears a stigma on its summit and all the stigmas radiate like the spokes of a wheel from a projection in the center. The flowers are fragrant.

Nymphaea odorata grows from Newfoundland to Florida and westward to Manitoba, Minnesota and Louisiana; also in Mexico, the West Indies and South America. The plant illustrated was found near Washington, D. C.

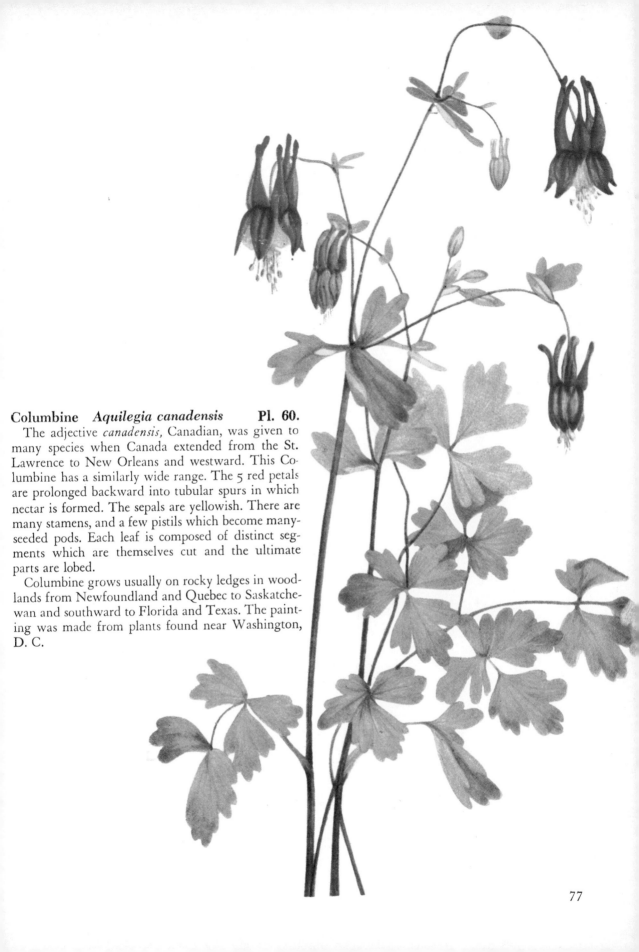

Columbine   *Aquilegia canadensis*   Pl. 60.

The adjective *canadensis,* Canadian, was given to many species when Canada extended from the St. Lawrence to New Orleans and westward. This Columbine has a similarly wide range. The 5 red petals are prolonged backward into tubular spurs in which nectar is formed. The sepals are yellowish. There are many stamens, and a few pistils which become many-seeded pods. Each leaf is composed of distinct segments which are themselves cut and the ultimate parts are lobed.

Columbine grows usually on rocky ledges in woodlands from Newfoundland and Quebec to Saskatchewan and southward to Florida and Texas. The painting was made from plants found near Washington, D. C.

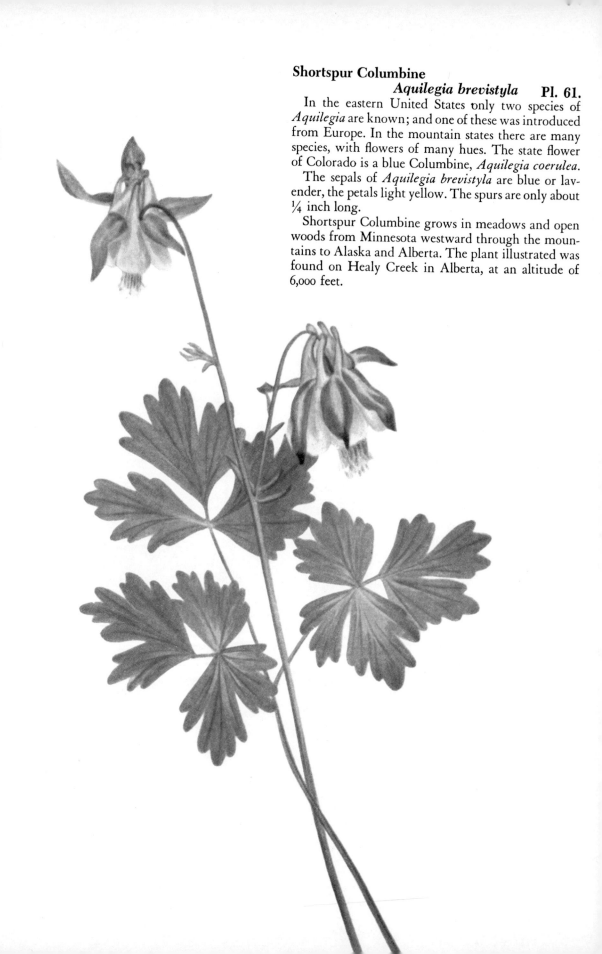

Shortspur Columbine
Aquilegia brevistyla   Pl. 61.

In the eastern United States only two species of *Aquilegia* are known; and one of these was introduced from Europe. In the mountain states there are many species, with flowers of many hues. The state flower of Colorado is a blue Columbine, *Aquilegia coerulea*.

The sepals of *Aquilegia brevistyla* are blue or lavender, the petals light yellow. The spurs are only about ¼ inch long.

Shortspur Columbine grows in meadows and open woods from Minnesota westward through the mountains to Alaska and Alberta. The plant illustrated was found on Healy Creek in Alberta, at an altitude of 6,000 feet.

Tall Buttercup
Ranunculus acris   Pl. 62.

The flowers of *Ranunculus* usually have 5 green sepals and 5 colored petals; the petals may be yellow or white, and in many species look as if they had been waxed and polished; this is due to a curious arrangement of the cells just under the surface. There is usually a small nectar-gland near the base. Each of the numerous pistils becomes an achene, a one-seeded fruit like a minute nut. The achenes of *Ranunculus acris* are somewhat flattened, with a thickened edge. The plant reaches a height of 3 feet.

The Tall Buttercup came from Europe, but is now almost as much at home in the eastern United States. It grows in fields and roadsides from Labrador to North Carolina and westward to Minnesota, Kansas and Oklahoma.

DFP

Avalanche Buttercup
Ranunculus suksdorfii　Pl. 63.

The cluster of pistils surrounded by stamens is plainly evident in the painting. The achenes of this species have long narrow beaks.

The Avalanche Buttercup, which has been recently classified as variety *suksdorfii* of *Ranunculus eschscholtzii,* grows in mountain meadows near timberline from Alaska to Washington in the Cascade Mountains and eastward to Montana in the Rockies. The painting was made from plants found near Field, British Columbia, at an altitude of 7,000 feet.

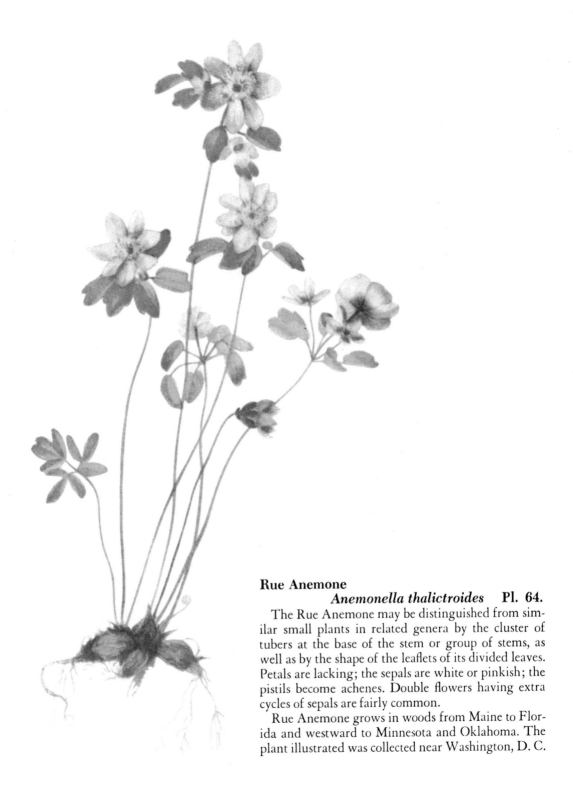

Rue Anemone
Anemonella thalictroides   **Pl. 64.**

The Rue Anemone may be distinguished from similar small plants in related genera by the cluster of tubers at the base of the stem or group of stems, as well as by the shape of the leaflets of its divided leaves. Petals are lacking; the sepals are white or pinkish; the pistils become achenes. Double flowers having extra cycles of sepals are fairly common.

Rue Anemone grows in woods from Maine to Florida and westward to Minnesota and Oklahoma. The plant illustrated was collected near Washington, D. C.

Columbia Windflower
Anemone deltoidea   Pl. 65.

The flowering stems of *Anemone deltoidea* arise from slender creeping underground stems, and reach a height of a foot. There is usually a single basal leaf divided into 3; and 3 leaves at a point where the one flower-stalk originates. The flowers of *Anemone* have sepals but no petals, many stamens, and a round or thimble-shaped head of pistils which become achenes. Windflower is a translation of the Greek word Anemone.

The Columbia Windflower is found in coniferous forests in the mountains of Washington, Oregon and northern California. The painting was made in Mt. Rainier National Park, Washington.

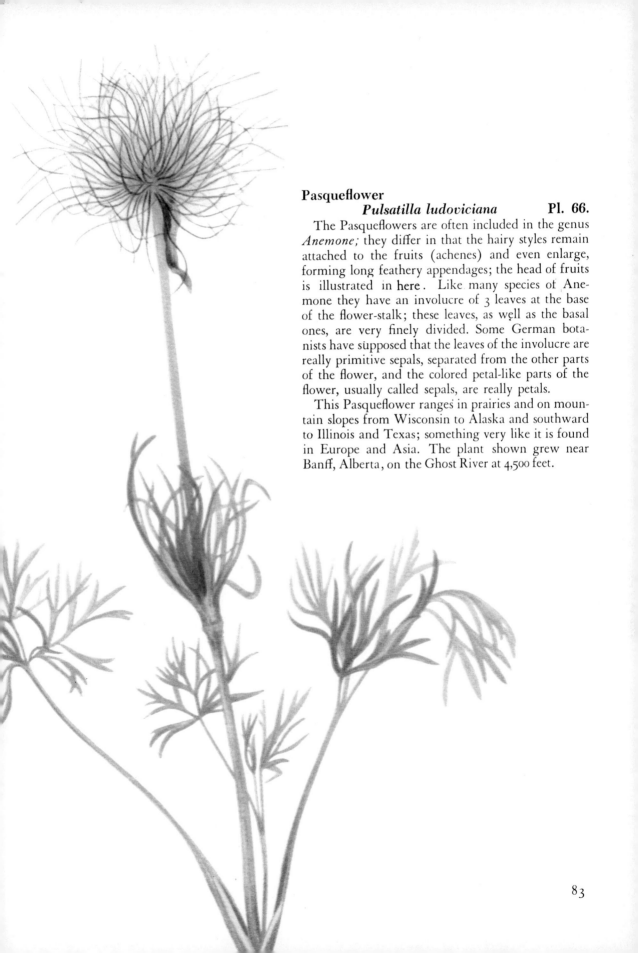

Pasqueflower
Pulsatilla ludoviciana   Pl. 66.

The Pasqueflowers are often included in the genus
Anemone; they differ in that the hairy styles remain
attached to the fruits (achenes) and even enlarge,
forming long feathery appendages; the head of fruits
is illustrated in here. Like many species of Anemone they have an involucre of 3 leaves at the base
of the flower-stalk; these leaves, as well as the basal
ones, are very finely divided. Some German botanists have supposed that the leaves of the involucre are
really primitive sepals, separated from the other parts
of the flower, and the colored petal-like parts of the
flower, usually called sepals, are really petals.

This Pasqueflower ranges in prairies and on mountain slopes from Wisconsin to Alaska and southward
to Illinois and Texas; something very like it is found
in Europe and Asia. The plant shown grew near
Banff, Alberta, on the Ghost River at 4,500 feet.

Western Pasqueflower
Pulsatilla occidentalis   Pl. 67.

The strictly western species of *Pulsatilla* differs in having the sepals white instead of purple (or white lightly marked with blue); and in the involucral leaves, which are slightly stalked. This plate shows plainly the large group of pistils surrounded by the numerous stamens.

Pulsatilla occidentalis occurs on mountain-sides from Alaska to California, extending eastward in the high mountains to Montana and Utah. The painting of this plate was made from plants that grew on Lake O'Hara near Lake Louise, Alberta, at an altitude of 4,000 feet.

Virgin's Bower
Clematis columbiana   **Pl. 68.**

This species has 3 broad leaflets to a stalk. The flowers vary from blue to purple. A common eastern species, *Clematis virginiana,* is also called Virgin's Bower. It has rather small whitish sepals but a conspicuous head of fruit.

Clematis columbiana is found in forests from British Columbia to Oregon east of the Cascade Mountains and eastward to Alberta, Colorado and Utah. The painting were made in British Columbia. Plate 6 was made from a plant collected near Field, on the slopes of Mt. Burgess, at an altitude of 6,500 feet.

Yellow Cucumber Tree
Magnolia cordata   Pl. 69.

The Yellow Cucumber Tree is often classified as a variety of *Magnolia acuminata*. It has smaller flowers with petals of a yellowish color. *Cordata* means "heart-shaped," and refers to the outline of some of the leaves.

Magnolia cordata is known in South Carolina, Georgia and Alabama, where it grows in rich woods.

papaw *Asimina triloba*   **Pl. 70.**

The flowers of Papaw appear in spring just before the leaves. Like the Magnolias, the Papaw has 3 sepals and 6 petals in 2 sets; the latter are dark purplish-brown in color. There are numerous stamens but only a few pistils, which become large pulpy edible fruits. These must not be confused with the tropical fruits also known as Papaw but which belong to an entirely different family. The fruits of *Asimina,* each containing many seeds, have a delicious odor but the flavor is disappointing. In the Ozark hills they are known as Poor Man's Banana. In parts of the range no fruit is formed. The tree is small, rarely more than 40 feet high.

Asimina triloba is found along streams in alluvial soil from New York to Florida and westward to Michigan, Nebraska and Texas. The painting was made from a plant on Plummer's Island in the Potomac River near Washington, D. C.

Creeping Mahonia *Mahonia repens* Pl. 71.

The stem creeps over the ground, rising only 6 or 8 inches above the surface. The flowers are small, yellow, with usually 3 sepals and 3 petals, 3 stamens and a single pistil. Another species of this genus, *Mahonia aquifolium,* is commonly called the Oregon Grape because of its blue berries; it is the state flower of Oregon. The genus is not related to the Grapes but to the Barberries.

Mahonia repens grows in open pine forests from British Columbia to northeastern California on the eastern slopes of the Cascade Mountains, and eastward to Alberta, Nebraska and New Mexico. The painting was made from a plant growing in Sinclair Canyon, British Columbia, at an altitude of 3,500 feet.

May-apple *Podophyllum peltatum* **Pl. 72.**

Though very different in general aspect from other members of the Barberry Family, May-apple has the same floral structure: 2 sepals, from 6 to 8 petals, a single pistil. The stamens are somewhat more numerous — from 12 to 18. The large stigma is visible in the painting. The pistil becomes a small green edible berry. A creeping stem grows beneath the ground, sending up either a single umbrella-shaped leaf, or a stem bearing 2 leaves and a flower at the junction of the leaf-stalks.

May-apple is found in woods and open places over a wide range from Quebec to Florida and westward to Minnesota and Texas. The plant illustrated grew near Washington, D. C.

Pale Corydalis
Corydalis sempervirens   Pl. 73.

The Fumitory Family is related to the Poppies. Its flowers have 2 sepals and 4 petals, 6 stamens, and a narrow pod like that of a Mustard. The petals are in 2 pairs. In *Corydalis* the upper petal of the outer pair has a hollow spur which projects backward over the flower stalk. The 2 inner petals cohere at their tips and bear a projecting wing. The stamens are in 2 groups of 3 each, the stalks united in each group. Other species of *Corydalis* have yellow flowers.

Pale Corydalis has a wide range from Newfoundland to Georgia and westward to Alaska; it grows in open rocky places. The plant illustrated grew in the valley of the Kootenai River in British Columbia, at at altitude of 4,000 feet.

Squirrel Corn

Dicentra canadensis **Pl. 74.**

Dicentra differs from *Corydalis* in having both of its outer petals spurred; the spurs in this species are short and broad. The ends of these petals spread apart to disclose the crested joined tips of the inner pair. At the base of the stem is the short underground stem covered with yellow tubers, the "squirrel corn."

Dicentra canadensis grows in woods from Nova Scotia and Quebec to North Carolina and westward to Minnesota and Missouri. The plant in the sketch was collected near Washington, D. C. Another member of this genus is the familiar Bleeding Heart often seen in gardens.

Mustard family. Cruciferae

Pitcher-plant family. Sarraceniaceae

The Sarraceniaceae are the Pitcher-plants. The 3 genera in the family have about 10 known species (besides many hybrids), all American and mostly North American. They are characterized by leaves shaped like pitchers, tubes, or trumpets. In the largest genus, *Sarracenia,* the inner surface of these leaves exudes a juice which contains digestive enzymes. The outer surface produces nectar. The structure of the cells and the presence of down-pointing hairs around and beneath the lip on the inner surface ensure that small insects attracted by the nectar will fall into the pitcher or tube and be unable to escape. Their bodies are digested in the liquid inside and the products are absorbed by the leaf, which is therefore carnivorous. The flower consists of 5 sepals and 5 petals, many stamens, and a curious 5-rayed umbrella-like structure in the middle which arises from the ovary and bears the stigmas on its margin. The fruit is a 5-chambered pod containing many seeds. All the species of this family described below grow in swamps, bogs, or other wet places.

The paintings were made (unless another source is given) from plants grown in the greenhouses of the U. S. Department of Agriculture in Washington, D. C.

Sundew family. Droseraceae

Saxifrage family. Saxifragaceae

SAXIFRAGE   SAXIFRAGA

There are about 250 species of Saxifrages, found mostly in the north temperate zone and farther north; some 65 species are known in North America. Their parts are generally in fives — 5 sepals, 5 petals, 10 stamens, with the stem tip (receptacle) often extending up around the ovary like a cup. The ovary has 2 chambers and is more or less divided into 2 lobes, with a style arising from each; the fruit is a small 2-beaked pod or capsule. The name means "rock breaker," and was given to them probably because many of them grow in crevices.

Witch Hazel family. Hamamelidaceae

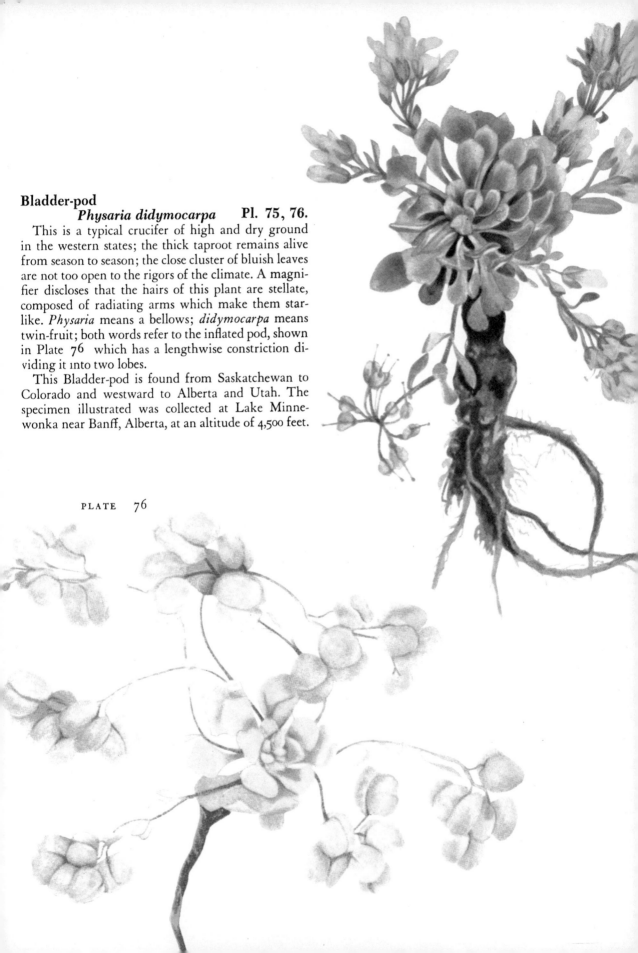

Bladder-pod
Physaria didymocarpa   Pl. 75, 76.

This is a typical crucifer of high and dry ground in the western states; the thick taproot remains alive from season to season; the close cluster of bluish leaves are not too open to the rigors of the climate. A magnifier discloses that the hairs of this plant are stellate, composed of radiating arms which make them starlike. *Physaria* means a bellows; *didymocarpa* means twin-fruit; both words refer to the inflated pod, shown in Plate 76 which has a lengthwise constriction dividing it into two lobes.

This Bladder-pod is found from Saskatchewan to Colorado and westward to Alberta and Utah. The specimen illustrated was collected at Lake Minnewonka near Banff, Alberta, at an altitude of 4,500 feet.

PLATE 76

◀**Pitcher-plant**

Sarracenia purpurea Pl. 77.

This is the widest-ranging and commonest species of the genus, growing from Labrador to Florida and westward to Saskatchewan, Iowa and Mississippi (the northern and southern plants are placed in separate varieties). It is the national flower of Newfoundland. Its pitchers are curved and broadly winged, up to 10 inches long. The sepals and petals vary from greenish to purple.

Hybrid Pitcher-plant
Sarracenia catesbaei Pl. 78.

This striking plant is a natural hybrid between *Sarracenia purpurea* and *Sarracenia flava,* and the specimen used for illustration was originally collected from a swamp near Quincy, Florida, where both the parental species were growing. There is evidence that the hybrid can perpetuate itself as if it were a good species. The plant was first described and named by the famous English botanist John Ray, in the seventeenth century.

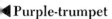

Purple-trumpet
Sarracenia drummondii Pl. 79.

The Purple-trumpet has erect leaves as tall as 30 inches. The flowers vary from greenish to deep purple. It grows from Georgia to Florida and Mississippi on the coastal plain.

Hooded Pitcher-plant
Sarracenia minor Pl. 80.

The lid, which in other species stands more or less erect, in this species is hood-like and curved over the opening of the long narrow pitcher. The leaves reach a length of 2 feet. *Sarracenia minor* grows from southern North Carolina to northern Florida on the coastal plain. The specimen used for illustration was found near Beaufort, South Carolina.

◀Venus' Fly-trap
Dionaea muscipula   Pl. 81.

The leaves of *Dionaea* are the fly-traps. Each half of the blade bears 3 rather large hairs, clearly visible in the painting; the surface is glandular and forms nectar attractive to insects. When an insect touches one of the hairs, the 2 halves of the leaf are folded rapidly together (as if the midrib were a hinge) and the long teeth at the margin interlock, so that the visitor is now a prisoner. The leaf then exudes a fluid which brings about the digestion of the animal body; the products of this digestion are absorbed by the leaf. After about 10 days the halves move slowly apart again. The flowers have their parts in fives.

Another genus of insect-catching plants belongs in this family: *Drosera*, Sundew.

Venus' Fly-trap grows in bogs and pinelands on the coastal plain in North and South Carolina. The painting was made from a plant growing in a greenhouse of the U. S. Department of Agriculture in Washington, D. C.

Red-stemmed Saxifrage
Saxifraga lyallii   Pl. 82.

The leaves are all basal. Not only is the stem red, but the reflexed sepals and the stamens as well; the petals are pink or white. The flowers are often double.

This Saxifrage grows on rocky ledges from Montana to Alaska and southward to Washington. The plant illustrated was found at Baker Lake near Lake Louise, Alberta, at an altitude of 6,500 feet.

Spotted Saxifrage
Saxifraga austromontana   Pl. 83.

This is another species which forms a matted mass of horizontal stems and narrow leaves. The red flower-stalks grow up to 6 inches high, each bearing a cluster of small flowers. The white petals are veined and spotted with dark red.

Spotted Saxifrage grows among rocks in the mountains from Alberta to Alaska and southward to New Mexico and Oregon. The plants shown were collected near Lake Louise, Alberta, at an altitude of 6,500 feet.

PLATE 84

100

Prickly Currant *Ribes lacustre* Pl. 84,85.

The Currants and Gooseberries form the genus *Ribes;* some botanists place them in separate genera; sometimes also they are separated from the Saxifrages and placed in a family of their own. In general the flower is like that of a Saxifrage: 5 sepals, 5 petals, 5 stamens; the ovary has but one chamber but bears a 2-cleft style. The distinctive features are that the ovary is wholly inferior, with the receptacle adhering around it and extending above it in the form of a cup or tube and that the fruit is a berry. The stem bears bristle. and spines; the latter occur just under the lateral branches, taking the place of the leaves which we should expect to find there. In this respect this Currant resembles the Gooseberries.

Prickly Currant grows in mountain meadows from Newfoundland to Alaska, extending southward to Massachusetts, Pennsylvania, Michigan, Colorado, Utah and California. The plants illustrated were collected in British Columbia; the flowering plant on the slopes of Mt. Wapta near Field, at an altitude of 7,000 feet; the fruiting specimen near Glacier Lake, at 6,000 feet.

Witch Hazel
Hamamelis virginiana   Pl. 86.

This plant has nothing to do with witches; the common name is derived from an Old English word meaning "pliable" and related to "weak." The use of the branches as divining rods for finding water is well known. The extract of the same name is obtained from the bark. The flowers resemble those of the preceding family in many ways: 4 sepals, 4 petals, 8 stamens, and an ovary (partly inferior) which becomes a 2-chambered, 2-beaked pod. The narrow petals are characteristic. This species flowers in the autumn after the leaves have been shed; other species (one found in the Midwest) flower in winter or early spring.

Witch Hazel grows along streams and in moist woods from Nova Scotia and Quebec to Florida and westward to Minnesota and Texas. The plant illustrated, which bears flowers and old pods, grew near Washington, D. C.

Rose family. Rosaceae   Page 104

The great Rose Family includes many well-known cultivated plants: Roses, Strawberries, Blackberries, Raspberries, Plums, Peaches, Cherries, Almonds. Sepals and petals are usually in fives, and grow, with numerous stamens, from the outer part of a cup or disc formed from the end of the flower-stalk and often called the receptacle. There are several or many pistils (one in *Prunus*). The leaves are usually attached singly, and each has a pair of small leaf-like appendages at the point where is joins the stem; these are the stipules.

BLACKBERRY AND RASPBERRY   *RUBUS*   Page 110

The large genus *Rubus* is one of the most difficult to understand. Botanists cannot even agree on what to call a species; one manual lists 205 species from northeastern North America, another only 24 — from almost the same range. The so-called berry is really a cluster of small succulent stone-fruits, each having the structure of a cherry, and each developed from one of the many pistils in the center of the flower. In the raspberries the entire cluster of fruits slips off from the receptacle, the knob which bears it; in the blackberries the small fruits fall singly from the receptacle.

Apple family. Malaceae   Page 112

The Apple Family is often united with the Rose Family; it is distinguished in having an inferior ovary. The ovary as usual becomes the fruit, but the enveloping parts of the stem-tip furnish most of the succulent tissue, the apple.

Bean family. Leguminosae   Page 113

The Bean Family is related to the Rose Family. It contains the Pea, Bean, Clover, Alfalfa, Sweet Pea, Lupine, Wisteria, Peanut, and other species familiar in cultivation, besides numerous weeds. Most of the genera have irregular flowers (i.e., not radially symmetric) described as papilionaceous (butterflylike): there are a standard, two wings and a keel; within the keel the 5 to 10 stamens surround the single pistil. The pistil becomes the pod, which usually splits into two halves, lengthwise, when ripe. Many genera, however, have flowers differing widely from this scheme, on which basis the family has been divided into three by some botanists.

Geranium family. Geraniaceae   Page 122

Milkwort family. Polygalaceae   Page 123

Hardhack *Spiraea tomentosa* Pl. 87.

The small flowers grow in a long spike-like cluster. The leaves are white and woolly on the under side, where also the veins are prominent. The fruits of *Spiraea* are small pods which open along one side. Other species of the genus are Bridal Wreath and Meadow-sweet.

Hardhack grows in meadows, old pastures, and wet places from Nova Scotia and New Brunswick to North Carolina and westward to Minnesota and Arkansas.

DFP

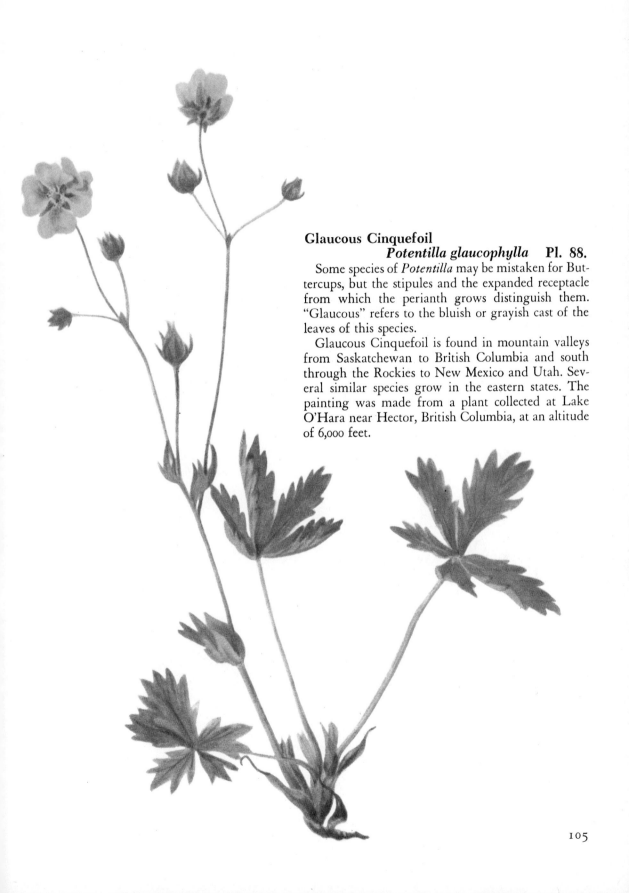

Glaucous Cinquefoil
Potentilla glaucophylla   Pl. 88.

Some species of *Potentilla* may be mistaken for Buttercups, but the stipules and the expanded receptacle from which the perianth grows distinguish them. "Glaucous" refers to the bluish or grayish cast of the leaves of this species.

Glaucous Cinquefoil is found in mountain valleys from Saskatchewan to British Columbia and south through the Rockies to New Mexico and Utah. Several similar species grow in the eastern states. The painting was made from a plant collected at Lake O'Hara near Hector, British Columbia, at an altitude of 6,000 feet.

PLATE 89

White Dryad *Dryas octopetala* **Pl. 89, 90.**

In spite of its botanical name, which means "8-petaled dryad," this species has from 8 to 10 petals. The Dryads are distinguished from several related genera by their simple leaves (i.e., they are not divided into several leaflets on one stalk, as are those of *Potentilla*). The White Dryad has leaves which are white and woolly, with prominent veins on the under side. The flower-stalk bears its single flower as much as 8 inches above the ground. Plate 90 shows the head of fruits with their hairy styles, like those of *Clematis* and *Pulsatilla*.

The White Dryad grows on high rocky ridges from Greenland to Alaska and southward to Colorado; also in Europe and Asia. The specimens illustrated came from Alberta; the flowering plant from the Skoki Valley near Lake Louise, at an altitude of 7,500 feet; the fruiting plant from the Siffleur River, at 6,500 feet.

Prairie Smoke *Sieversia triflora* **Pl. 91.**

Notice that *Sieversia* has not only petals and sepals but a third ring of parts; these are called bractlets. The very long styles on the fruits are hairy except at the tip. The petals vary in color from yellowish to purple. The whole plant is softly hairy and fringed with long cilia ("eyelashes").

It grows in prairies and rocky places from New York to British Columbia and southward into Illinois, Iowa, Nebraska, New Mexico and California. The eastern and western plants are placed in separate varieties of the species.

Pale-leaved Strawberry
Fragaria glauca **Pl. 92.**

The flower of a Strawberry has a ring of bractlets like those of *Sieversia*. The so-called fruit, the edible berry, is the enlarged and succulent receptacle in the center of the flower, and the so-called seeds which are found upon it are the fruits formed from the numerous pistils.

Fragaria glauca is found in the mountains from British Columbia to New Mexico and eastward to South Dakota. It closely resembles *Fragaria virginiana,* which is the common wild strawberry growing in meadows and on hillsides in the eastern states. The cultivated strawberry is of hybrid origin. The specimen illustrated was collected on Baker Creek near Lake Louise, Alberta, at an altitude of 5,000 feet.

Wild Rose *Rosa bourgeauiana*   Pl. 94. ▶

The flower of a Rose has its parts borne in or on a deep cup-shaped receptacle (like that of *Prunus*). There are many pistils, each becoming a hard seed-like fruit; and the entire receptacle becomes enlarged and succulent, a favorite food for birds and sometimes used by man.

There are many wild species of *Rosa*, often difficult to identify. *Rosa bourgeauiana* grows in woods from Ontario westward to Mackenzie and Colorado. The plant illustrated was found in Alberta at Lake Minnewonka near Banff, at an altitude of 4,500 feet.

Red Dewberry *Rubus pedatus*   Pl. 93.

The Dewberries are creeping species often found in old fields and on roadside banks. *Rubus pedatus* is a western representative of this group. It grows from Alaska to California and eastward to Alberta and Idaho. The plant illustrated was found in the valley of the Vermilion River, Alberta, at an altitude of 6,000 feet.

Wild Sweet Crab *Malus coronaria* Pl. 95.

This is the common Wild Crab of the northeastern states; other species are found in the Southeast and Midwest. It is a tree 20 feet or more high. The 5 petals, 5 sepals and numerous stamens all seem to grow from the summit of the inferior ovary; the latter becomes the crabapple, which is still crowned by the withered sepals and stamens. The 5 styles are separate nearly to the base. The leaves are rather coarsely toothed, often slightly lobed.

Malus coronaria is found in open woods and thickets from New York to Georgia and westward to Michigan, Kansas and Alabama. The painting was made near Washington, D. C.

Partridge-Pea *Cassia fasciculata* Pl. 96.

Cassia has a flower only slightly irregular, the 5 petals being a little unequal. There are 5 to 10 unequal stamens; some may be imperfect or of different colors from the others. Leaves and pods of some species are used medicinally under the name of Senna.

Partridge-pea is common in old fields and roadsides from Massachusetts and Ontario to Florida and westward to Minnesota, South Dakota and Texas.

DFP

Wild Lupine *Lupinus perennis*   **Pl. 97.**

This is the eastern species of a genus which is more common westward, where many species have been described. The Texas Bluebonnet, the state flower, is a lupine. The leaves are divided palmately, i.e., the leaflets radiate in a way suggestive of the fingers of a hand. The 10 stamens of the flower are all joined in a tube around the pistil.

Lupine grows usually in sandy soil from Maine to Florida and westward to Minnesota and Louisiana. The painting was made near Washington, D. C.

Prairie Clover

Petalostemum purpureum **Pl. 98.**

The flowers grow in a close head like that of clover, blooming from the base up. Each flower has a standard and 4 smaller petals all much alike which adhere to the tube formed by the 5 stamens. The pod contains only 1 or 2 seeds. *Purpureum* means "purple"; the crimson shown in the painting was formerly known as purple, and the latter word must be understood in this sense in old names of plants.

This species of *Petalostemum* grows in dry grassy places from Indiana to Alberta and southward to Kentucky, Arkansas, Texas and New Mexico. The plant illustrated was found on a prairie east of Glacier National Park, Montana.

115

Milk-vetch *Astragalus bourgovii* Pl. 99.

The very large genus *Astragalus* (perhaps 1,500 species) is especially abundant in the western states; the species are difficult to identify. The leaves are pinnately divided in the manner shown in the illustrations. The flowers are of the usual papilionaceous type, with 9 of the 10 stamens united to form a tube open along the top; the tenth stamen lies in this opening. The characteristic flower-clusters also are shown in the paintings. The pods are often thick and hard and in many species divided into two compartments, or almost so, and deeply grooved on one or both edge Some of the species with thick pods are called Ground plum. A number of western species are poisonous an known as Loco-weed.

Astragalus bourgovii has a rather flat oblong po about ½ inch long, bearing black hairs. It grows i the mountains from South Dakota to British Colum bia. The plant illustrated was collected in Burges Pass near Field, British Columbia, at an altitude o 7,500 feet.

Alpine Milk-vetch

     Astragalus alpinus **Pl. 100.**

 This species has a narrow tapering pod which, if cut across, has an outline like a heart upside-down; the groove along the lower edge nearly divides the pod in two lengthwise. It is covered with black hairs and is rather leathery.

 Astragalus alpinus grows on gravelly banks in arctic regions around the world, in North America from Labrador to Alaska and southward into Vermont, Wisconsin, Colorado, Idaho and Alberta. The painting was made from a plant collected on Johnson Creek in Alberta at an altitude of 6,000 feet.

Wisteria *Wisteria frutescens* **Pl. 101.**

Most species of *Wisteria* come from eastern Asia; several are known in cultivation; 2 are natives of our southeastern states. *Wisteria frutescens* is a shrubby climber, its stems twining. The sickle-shaped keel encloses stamens arranged as in *Astragalus,* 9 joined and 1 separate. The smooth pod contains a few large seeds.

This *Wisteria* grows in moist woods and on river banks from southern Virginia to Florida and Alabama. The plant shown was found near Savannah, Georgia.

Sweet Vetch

Hedysarum mackenzii Pl. 102.

The pod of *Hedysarum* is compressed and composed of a series of joints, which easily separate. Those of *Hedysarum mackenzii* are round. Its flowers are usually described as purple, but the color varies to light shades and, as shown in the painting, even to white; they are very fragrant. Notice also the long sharp sepals. The roots have been used for food.

Hedysarum mackenzii grows on dry slopes, often among shrubs, in Arctic America, extending southward to Alberta and eastern Oregon; also to Newfoundland. The painting was made from plants growing near Lake Louise, Alberta, at an altitude of 8,000 feet.

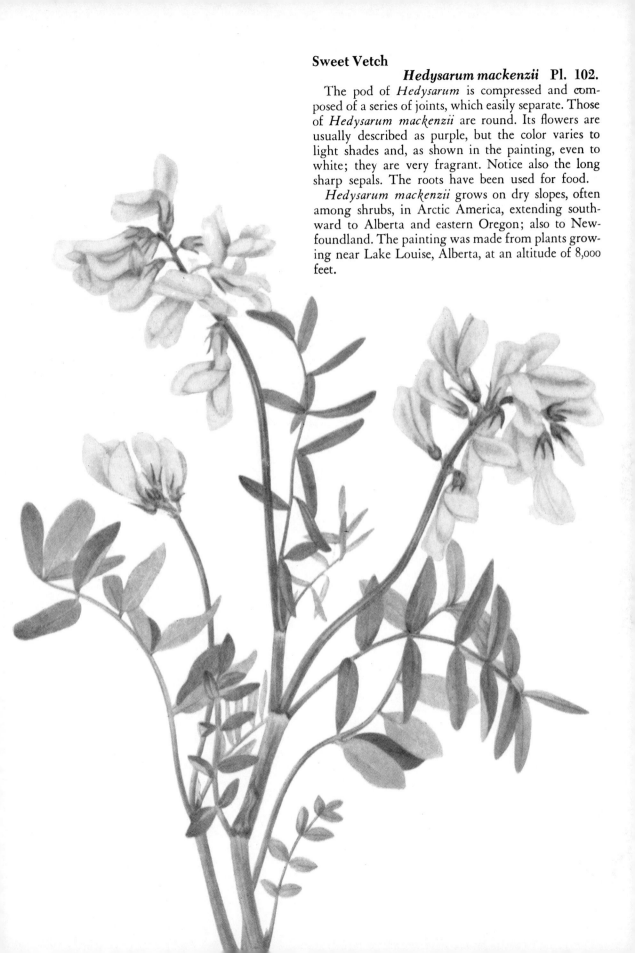

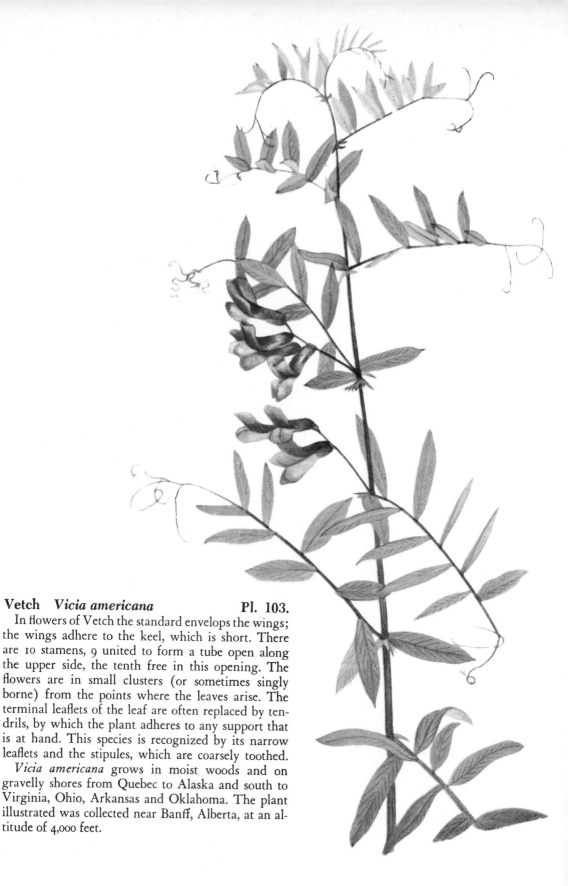

Vetch *Vicia americana*   Pl. 103.

In flowers of Vetch the standard envelops the wings;
the wings adhere to the keel, which is short. There
are 10 stamens, 9 united to form a tube open along
the upper side, the tenth free in this opening. The
flowers are in small clusters (or sometimes singly
borne) from the points where the leaves arise. The
terminal leaflets of the leaf are often replaced by tendrils, by which the plant adheres to any support that
is at hand. This species is recognized by its narrow
leaflets and the stipules, which are coarsely toothed.

Vicia americana grows in moist woods and on
gravelly shores from Quebec to Alaska and south to
Virginia, Ohio, Arkansas and Oklahoma. The plant
illustrated was collected near Banff, Alberta, at an altitude of 4,000 feet.

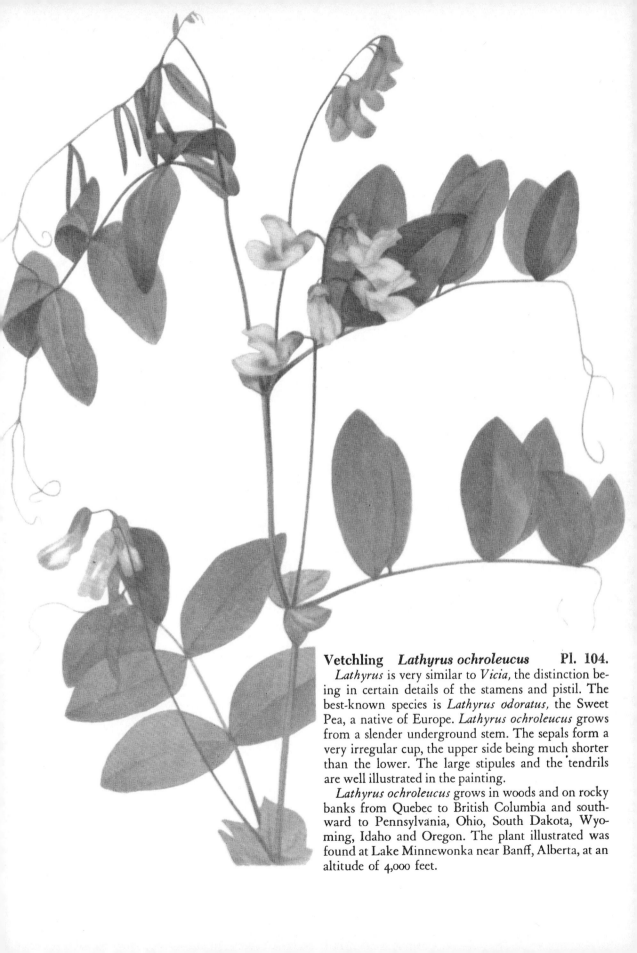

Vetchling   *Lathyrus ochroleucus*   **Pl. 104.**

Lathyrus is very similar to *Vicia,* the distinction being in certain details of the stamens and pistil. The best-known species is *Lathyrus odoratus,* the Sweet Pea, a native of Europe. *Lathyrus ochroleucus* grows from a slender underground stem. The sepals form a very irregular cup, the upper side being much shorter than the lower. The large stipules and the tendrils are well illustrated in the painting.

Lathyrus ochroleucus grows in woods and on rocky banks from Quebec to British Columbia and southward to Pennsylvania, Ohio, South Dakota, Wyoming, Idaho and Oregon. The plant illustrated was found at Lake Minnewonka near Banff, Alberta, at an altitude of 4,000 feet.

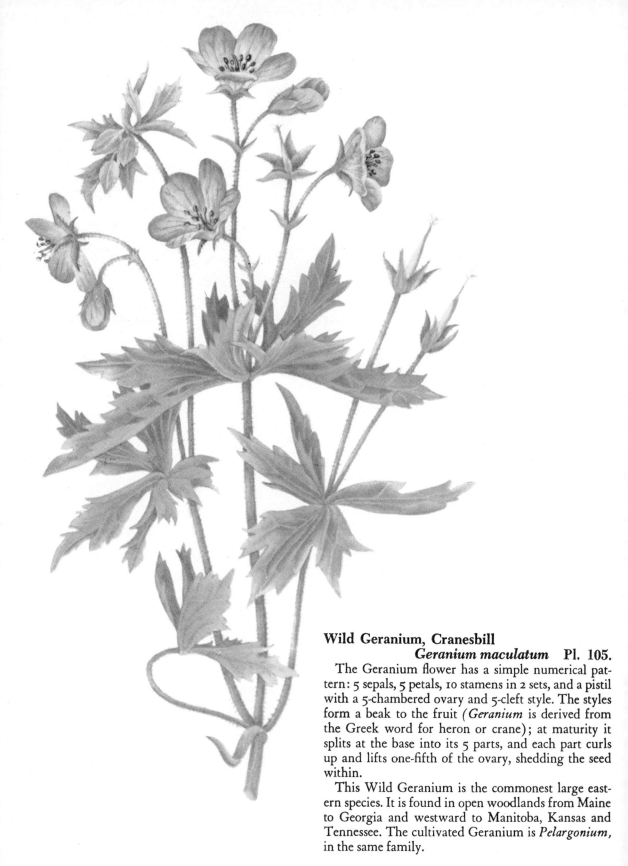

Wild Geranium, Cranesbill
Geranium maculatum **Pl. 105.**

The Geranium flower has a simple numerical pattern: 5 sepals, 5 petals, 10 stamens in 2 sets, and a pistil with a 5-chambered ovary and 5-cleft style. The styles form a beak to the fruit (*Geranium* is derived from the Greek word for heron or crane); at maturity it splits at the base into its 5 parts, and each part curls up and lifts one-fifth of the ovary, shedding the seed within.

This Wild Geranium is the commonest large eastern species. It is found in open woodlands from Maine to Georgia and westward to Manitoba, Kansas and Tennessee. The cultivated Geranium is *Pelargonium,* in the same family.

Orange Milkwort

Polygala lutea Pl. 106.

The *Polygala* flower is irregular: there are 5 sepals, the 2 lateral being much larger and colored like the petals; 3 petals, the lowest keel-like, all joined with each other and with the 6 or 8 stamens, which are also more or less united; the ovary has 2 chambers. The name refers, not to any milky juice, but to the reputed virtue of some species in increasing the flow of milk.

Orange Milkwort is found in pinelands and boggy places on the coastal plain from New York to Florida and Louisiana. The painting was made at Beaufort, South Carolina.

Fringed Milkwort
Polygala paucifolia Pl. 107.

This species differs from the preceding in having its flowers borne singly; they vary from red-purple to white. The keel petal is cut at the tip into narrow segments, forming a delicate fringe.

Fringed Milkwort grows in the mountains from Quebec to Georgia and westward to Manitoba, Minnesota, Illinois and Tennessee. The specimen illustrated was collected near Pocono Manor, Pennsylvania.

Crowberry *Empetrum nigrum* Pl. 108.

The Crowberry suggests a Heath; but the flowers lack petals; there are 3 sepals and 3 stamens; the stigma has 6 to 9 rays.

Crowberry is found in boggy places in arctic regions around the world, extending southward in America to Newfoundland, New England, northern Michigan, Minnesota, Alberta and northern California. The plant sketched grew in Vermilion Pass near Castle Station, Alberta, at an altitude of 5,000 feet.

Yaupon, Cassena *Ilex vomitoria* Pl. 109.

This is a shrub or small tree with thick evergreen leaves which are indented on the edges but not toothed. The flower parts are in fours. An infusion of the leaves is drunk like tea; if the brew is strong, it has emetic properties, whence the botanical name. The well-known South American drink maté is made from a species of *Ilex*.

Yaupon grows in sandy woodlands from southeastern Virginia to Florida and westward to Arkansas and Texas. The plant illustrated was found near Beaufort, South Carolina.

Red Maple *Acer rubrum* **Pl. 110.**

The flowers of Red Maple are among the earliest flowers of spring, appearing long before the leaves. Staminate flowers are shown in the painting; other flowers have pistils only, and still others have both stamens and pistils. The petals are similar to the sepals in size and color. The 2-lobed ovary grows a pair of wings and becomes the maple "key," which in this species is also bright red. The leaves are palmately lobed, with sharp notches between the lobes, their under side whitish and often downy.

Red Maple has a wide range, from Newfoundland and Quebec to Florida and westward to Manitoba, Missouri and Texas; it is best developed in low woods and swamps. The specimen illustrated was collected at Spring Lake, New Jersey.

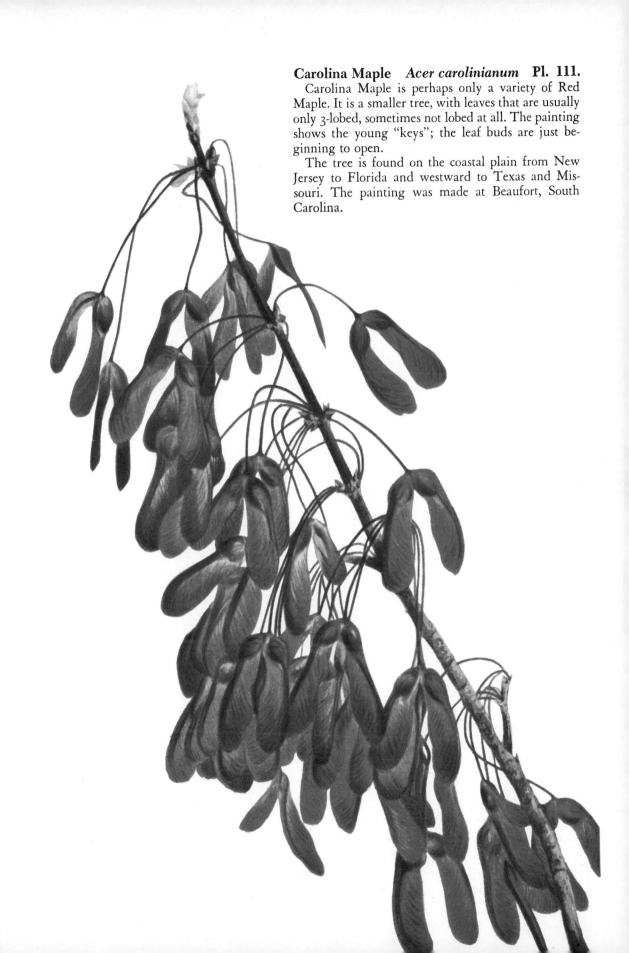

Carolina Maple *Acer carolinianum* **Pl. 111.**

Carolina Maple is perhaps only a variety of Red Maple. It is a smaller tree, with leaves that are usually only 3-lobed, sometimes not lobed at all. The painting shows the young "keys"; the leaf buds are just beginning to open.

The tree is found on the coastal plain from New Jersey to Florida and westward to Texas and Missouri. The painting was made at Beaufort, South Carolina.

Red Buckeye   *Aesculus pavia*   **Pl. 112.**

The Buckeyes have large irregular flowers: 5 sepals, 4 or 5 petals which are unequal in size, usually 7 stamens and a 3-chambered pistil which becomes a round leathery fruit. The fruit is prickly in some species, but not in this one. The seed is hard and shining, somewhat resembling a Chestnut; the Horse Chestnut comes from the European tree of the same name, from which the family name is taken. All the species have paired leaves divided palmately into several leaflets. Most of them have yellowish petals.

Red Buckeye grows in woods and thickets from Virginia to Florida and Louisiana. The painting was made at Beaufort, South Carolina.

Jewelweed, Touch-me-not
Impatiens capensis **Pl. 113.**

The flowers of Jewelweed hang on their slender stalks. There are 3 sepals, the lower one petal-like and expanded into a sac which is prolonged backward into a bent hollow spur; and 3 petals. The 5-chambered ovary becomes a pod which splits open at a touch into 5 valves which curl up and scatter the seeds.

Jewelweed is an annual plant; it forms dense lush stands in ravines and along streams from Newfoundland to South Carolina and westward to Saskatchewan, Missouri and Oklahoma. It has been introduced into Europe. The Balsam grown in gardens is also in this genus.

DFP

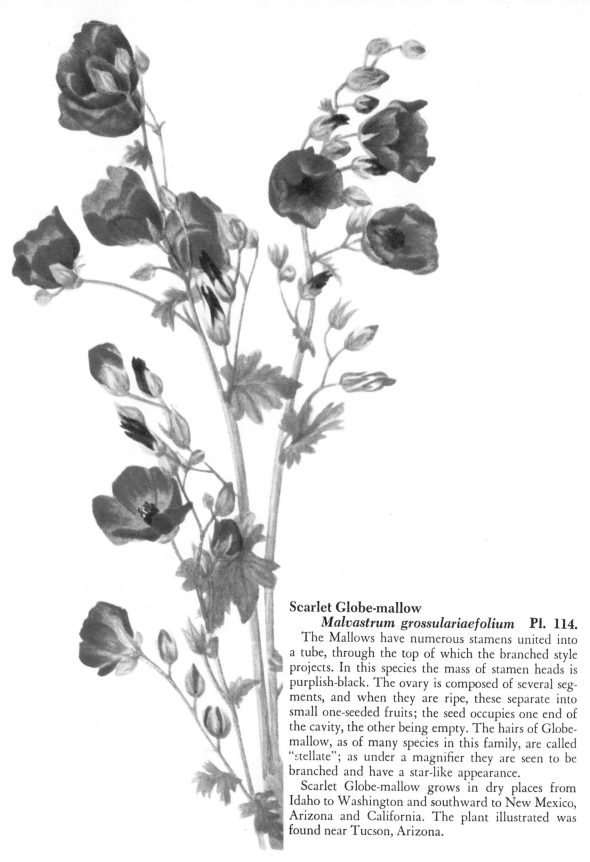

Scarlet Globe-mallow
Malvastrum grossulariaefolium Pl. 114.

The Mallows have numerous stamens united into a tube, through the top of which the branched style projects. In this species the mass of stamen heads is purplish-black. The ovary is composed of several segments, and when they are ripe, these separate into small one-seeded fruits; the seed occupies one end of the cavity, the other being empty. The hairs of Globe-mallow, as of many species in this family, are called "stellate"; as under a magnifier they are seen to be branched and have a star-like appearance.

Scarlet Globe-mallow grows in dry places from Idaho to Washington and southward to New Mexico, Arizona and California. The plant illustrated was found near Tucson, Arizona.

Rose Mallow

Hibiscus moscheutos Pl. 115.

Rose Mallow is a shrub reaching a height of 6 feet. The genus *Hibiscus* is a large one, recognizable by the narrow bracts which surround the sepals and by the stamens which bear their heads at various levels along the tube instead of all at the tip. The ovary is composed of 5 segments and the style has 5 branches.

Other species of *Hibiscus* are the Rose of Sharon, a native of Asia, and Okra; other members of the family are Hollyhock and Cotton.

Hibiscus moscheutos grows in marshes, mostly near the coast, from Connecticut to Florida, Texas and Missouri.

DFP

Tall St. John's Wort
Hypericum pyramidatum   Pl. 116.

The St. John's Worts often have numerous stamens joined at their bases into a number of bunches; there are 5 such bunches in this species. The ovary has 5 chambers and 5 styles. The leaves contain glands which make translucent spots. In other species the petals are spotted with black glands. Some of these species are common roadside weeds.

The Tall St. John's Wort, which may grow to 6 feet in height, is found in moist meadows and thickets from Quebec to Maryland and westward to Manitoba and Kansas.

DFP

Mexican Fremontia
Fremontia mexicana   Pl. 117.

This shrub is evergreen, as tall as 20 feet. The flowers have no petals, but 5 large sepals colored like petals; there are also small bracts outside the sepals. The 5 stamens are partly united. The 5-chambered ovary forms a pod which splits open in 5 lines. The leaves are densely covered on the under side with a felt of whitish hairs; these hairs are branched (stellate).

Fremontia mexicana grows in the open chaparral of southern California and southward into Mexico. The painting was made in Los Angeles. The species is closely allied to *Fremontia californica*.

Franklinia *Franklinia alatamaha* **Pl. 118.**

Franklinia has had a curious history. It was discovered by John and William Bartram on the coastal plain in Georgia in 1765, and has never been seen growing wild since 1790; it has been widely cultivated. It is a tall shrub or tree, up to 30 feet high, which flowers in the autumn; the flowers are fragrant.

The plant illustrated was cultivated at Whitesbog, New Jersey.

Violet family. Violaceae

VIOLET *VIOLA*

The Violet flower has a lower petal which projects backward as a spur. There are 5 stamens which fit closely around the style, holding their pollen, as it were, in a basket; the 2 lower ones bear nectaries which extend into the spur. An insect penetrating into the spur must touch these projecting glands and disturb the stamens, which shed their pollen on the visitor; this pollen may be rubbed off on the stigma of the next flower visited. There are also flowers which never open but fertilize themselves; they grow usually near the base of the plant, and produce more fruit than the ordinary flowers. The ovary is not divided; it forms a small pod with 3 rows of seeds attached to the 3 valves into which it splits when ripe.

Passion Flower family. Passifloraceae

Cactus family. Cactaceae

Many succulent or prickly plants are commonly known as Cactus; but the name is technically reserved for a family of American plants. The stems of these plants are much enlarged and contain considerable liquid; leaves are not formed, or only rudiments which fall early. The flowers have numerous sepals and petals in several rows and with the end of the stalk form a tube which not only invests the ovary but rises above it and bears the stamens on its inner surface. The ovary has but one cavity, and there is one style which supports a number of stigmas.

Oleaster family. Elaeagnaceae

Evening Primrose family. Onagraceae

Ginseng family. Araliaceae

Dogwood family. Cornaceae

Birdfoot Violet *Viola pedata* Pl. 119.

The Birdfoot Violet belongs to the group known as "stemless" Violets; their stems are short and thick and grow underground. There are 2 forms of the species; in one the 2 upper petals are dark purple, as shown in the painting; in the other all the petals are light blue. The leaves also vary greatly in outline.

Viola pedata grows in open places, often on rocky slopes, from Maine to Florida and westward to Minnesota and Texas; in parts of the Midwest it is common. The painting was made near Washington, D.C.

Smooth Yellow Violet

Viola eriocarpa **Pl. 120.**

The leaves and stem of this species are smooth or almost so; the capsule may be woolly (this is the meaning of *eriocarpa*) or, in a variety, smooth.

Viola eriocarpa is found in woods and low meadows from Nova Scotia to Georgia and westward to Manitoba and Texas. The plant illustrated grew on Plummer's Island in the Potomac River near Washington, D. C.

Purple Violet *Viola adunca* Pl. 121.

The form of *Viola adunca* which grows in the eastern states has long stems which tend to lie on the ground. In the high mountains of the west this diminutive form is found which resembles one of the "stemless" blue Violets. The lowland form is downy, the mountain form smooth.

Viola adunca is found from Quebec and New England westward to Alaska and California. The plant illustrated was collected at Bow Lake near Lake Louise, Alberta, at an altitude of 6,000 feet.

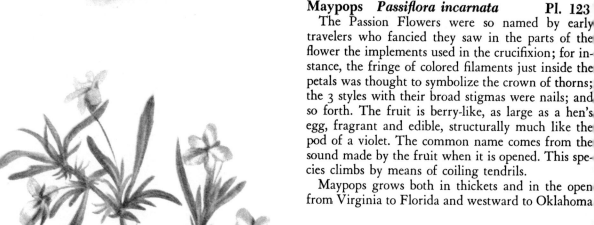

Maypops *Passiflora incarnata* Pl. 123

The Passion Flowers were so named by early travelers who fancied they saw in the parts of the flower the implements used in the crucifixion; for instance, the fringe of colored filaments just inside the petals was thought to symbolize the crown of thorns; the 3 styles with their broad stigmas were nails; and so forth. The fruit is berry-like, as large as a hen's egg, fragrant and edible, structurally much like the pod of a violet. The common name comes from the sound made by the fruit when it is opened. This species climbs by means of coiling tendrils.

Maypops grows both in thickets and in the open from Virginia to Florida and westward to Oklahoma.

Johnny Jump-up *Viola rafinesquii* Pl. 122.

The small flowers of this species vary greatly in color from almost white or yellowish to purple with a yellow "eye." The stipules are large and cut into narrow segments, giving the base of the leaf a feathery appearance.

Viola rafinesquii grows in fields and roadsides from New York to Georgia and westward to Colorado and Texas. In places it is so abundant that it colors the fields blue. The plant sketched grew in Rock Creek Park in Washington, D. C.

Strawberry Cactus
> *Echinocereus lloydii* Pl. 124.

The name comes from the berry-like appearance of the small stem, which consists of a single segment. The fruit is edible, the spines being easily removed.

This species grows only in western Texas.

Buffalo Berry

Shepherdia canadensis Pl. 125.

Buffalo Berry is a shrub about 6 feet tall. The leaves are smooth on the upper side, silvery and rather rusty with small scales on the lower side. The flowers are small, yellowish, either staminate or pistillate, the sepals 4. The so-called berry is actually formed by the sepals, which are joined and enclose the ovary. A related species has a better right to the name Buffalo Berry; it was much esteemed by the Indians for food.

Shepherdia canadensis grows in rocky or sandy places from Newfoundland to Alaska and southward to New York, Indiana, New Mexico and Arizona. The specimen illustrated was collected near Hector Station, British Columbia, at an altitude of 5,000 feet.

Silverberry
Elaeagnus commutata   **Pl. 126.**

Elaeagnus differs from *Shepherdia* chiefly in having stamens and pistils in the same flower, and in having the fleshy united sepals enclosing a hard nut-like fruit. Some Asiatic species are well known in cultivation under the names of Oleaster or Russian Olive.

Elaeagnus commutata grows on rocky hillsides from Quebec to Yukon and southward to Minnesota, Nebraska and Utah. The flowering specimen of Plate 237 was collected on the Ghost River in Alberta, at an altitude of 4,000 feet.

Evening Primrose
Oenothera biennis Pl. 127.

The family is recognized by its generally 4-parted flowers with an inferior ovary. In *Oenothera* there are 4 reflexed sepals, 4 petals, 8 stamens; the style bears a 4-parted stigma; the pod splits into 4 parts. *Oenothera biennis* is a highly variable group of plants common in old pastures and roadsides; the dead stalks and dried pods are a familiar sight. It is found from Quebec to Florida and westward to Manitoba, Kansas and Texas.

DFP

Broad-leaved Willow-herb
                 Epilobium latifolium **Pl. 128.**
    In this species the leaves are broad *(latifolium)*
and those beneath the flowers are more like the other
leaves. The style has no hairs.
    Epilobium latifolium is found on shores and ledges
from Greenland to Alaska and southward to Newfoundland, Quebec, South Dakota, Colorado and Oregon; also in Europe and Asia. The painting shows a
plant which grew near Glacier, British Columbia, at
an altitude of 3,500 feet.

Devil's Club *Oplopanax horridus* **Pl. 129.**

Devil's Club is an ill-scented plant with sharp stiff spines that make it a serious problem to one who walks where it grows (*horridus* means "bristling" or "prickly"). The petals are greenish-white; sepals are lacking. There are 5 stamens and an inferior ovary with 2 styles.

Devil's Club is found by streams and in moist woods from Montana to Alaska and Oregon; also on Isle Royale, Michigan. The plant illustrated grew near Field, British Columbia, at an altitude of 4,000 feet.

148

Bunchberry, Dwarf Cornel
Cornus canadensis   **Pl. 131.**

Bunchberry sends up its shoots from a woody underground stem. The "flowers" are flower-clusters like those of Flowering Dogwood. The small true flowers are generally white; those illustrated are unusual in their red tint. There is also a form with pink bracts.

Bunchberry grows in moist acid soil in woods or bogs from Greenland and Labrador to Alaska and southward to New Jersey, Kentucky, Wisconsin, South Dakota, Idaho and California; also in northeastern Asia. The painting of this specimen was made at Lake Louise, Alberta, at an altitude of 5,000 feet.

Flowering Dogwood
Cornus florida   **Pl. 130.**

All Dogwoods have flowers; this species owes its common name to the clusters of flowers surrounded by 4 enlarged bud-scales (bracts) which resemble white petals. The individual small yellow flowers and red fruits are much like those of the preceding species in structure. The leaves also are characteristic of the genus: the veins leave the midrib near its base and curve forward parallel to the margin. Forms are known with pink and red "flowers," and one with yellow fruits. The wood is hard (which is the meaning of *Cornus*). A bitter principle obtained from the bark has been used as a tonic and in the treatment of malaria.

Flowering Dogwood grows in woods from Maine to Florida and westward to Kansas and Texas; a subspecies is found in Mexico; related species occur in the Pacific States and in Asia. The specimen used in making this plate was found near Washington, D. C.

Heath family. Ericaceae   Page 151

The Heath Family has the sepals united into a tube or cup; the petals also are united, at least by their lower parts. The parts of a flower are in fours or fives. The fruit is a dry pod in most genera. The leaves are undivided, usually attached singly. Our species of this family are found mostly in boggy, acid soils, where their roots are probably associated with certain fungi, and are characteristic of high mountains and northern forests; many other species, however, are natives of the southern hemisphere and of the tropics.

RHODODENDRON AND AZALEA   *RHODODENDRON*   Page 152

This large and well-known genus has often been divided into two: *Rhododendron,* with evergreen leaves; and *Azalea,* which sheds its leaves in winter. The sepals are very small. The petals are joined at the base, and often differ in size and shape, so that the flower is irregular. There are 5 or 10 long stamens; the pollen is discharged through pores in the ends instead of through a split. The 5-chambered ovary bears a long style. The species have hybridized freely both in nature and in cultivation, and are difficult to identify.

Wintergreen family.   Pyrolaceae   Page 153

Blueberry family.   Vacciniaceae   Page 156

The Blueberry Family resembles the Heaths in many ways, but the ovary is inferior, and the berry develops from the ovary and the surrounding parts of the stem-tip; the remains of the sepals may be found on the top of the berry. The flower parts are in fours or fives; the petals are joined. The plants are woody.

Diapensia family.   Diapensiaceae   Page 158

Primrose family.   Primulaceae   Page 159

The Primrose Family is known by having 5 petals united at least at their bases and 5 stamens attached to the petals and situated opposite to them (rather than opposite to the gaps between them); the pistil is not divided into compartments; the numerous ovules are attached to a small knob which rises from the base of the cavity.

Olive family.   Oleaceae   Page 161

Logania family.   Loganiaceae   Page 162

Tar-flower   *Befaria racemosa*   Pl. 132.

Tar-flower is an evergreen shrub reaching a height of 8 feet. There are 6 or 7 petals and sepals and twice as many stamens. The petals are separate almost to the base.

Tar-flower grows in pinelands on the coastal plain from Georgia to Florida. Its closest relatives are in Mexico and South America. The plant shown in the painting was gathered near Jacksonville, Florida.

Smooth Azalea
Rhododendron arborescens   Pl. 133.

This species is a tall shrub or a tree up to 20 feet high, almost free from any hairiness. The petals are white or pink. The 5 stamens and the long style are clearly shown in the painting. Smooth Azalea grows in upland woods from Pennsylvania to Georgia and westward to Kentucky and Alabama. The plant illustrated was found near Linville, South Carolina, at the foot of Grandfather Mountain.

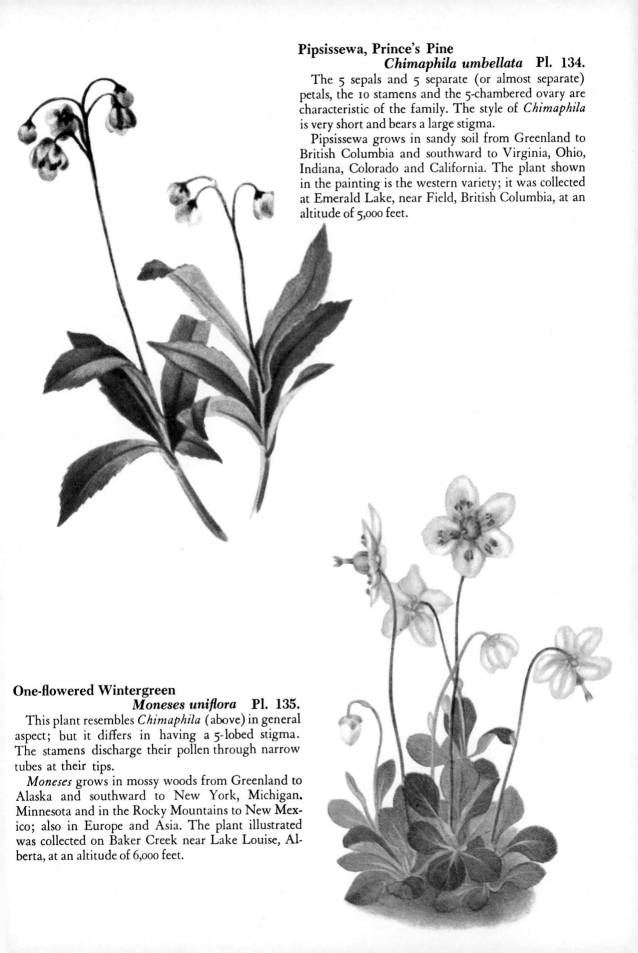

Pipsissewa, Prince's Pine
Chimaphila umbellata Pl. 134.

The 5 sepals and 5 separate (or almost separate) petals, the 10 stamens and the 5-chambered ovary are characteristic of the family. The style of *Chimaphila* is very short and bears a large stigma.

Pipsissewa grows in sandy soil from Greenland to British Columbia and southward to Virginia, Ohio, Indiana, Colorado and California. The plant shown in the painting is the western variety; it was collected at Emerald Lake, near Field, British Columbia, at an altitude of 5,000 feet.

One-flowered Wintergreen
Moneses uniflora Pl. 135.

This plant resembles *Chimaphila* (above) in general aspect; but it differs in having a 5-lobed stigma. The stamens discharge their pollen through narrow tubes at their tips.

Moneses grows in mossy woods from Greenland to Alaska and southward to New York, Michigan, Minnesota and in the Rocky Mountains to New Mexico; also in Europe and Asia. The plant illustrated was collected on Baker Creek near Lake Louise, Alberta, at an altitude of 6,000 feet.

Indian Pipe *Monotropa uniflora* **Pl. 136.**

This well-known plant lacks the green color which enables most flowering plants to make their own food from materials in the soil and the air, and must live like the fungi on organic materials; for this reason it is found growing in leaf-mold under trees. There are several irregularly placed scale-like sepals (or perhaps they are bracts). The petals are thickened toward their ends. Each stamen opens by two clefts across the top.

Indian Pipe is found from Newfoundland to Washington and southward to Florida, California and Central America; also in eastern Asia. The specimen shown grew on Mt. Desert Island, Maine.

Pinesap   *Hypopitys monotropa*   Pl. 137.

Pinesap differs from Indian Pipe in having several flowers at the summit of the stem. It grows up to a foot high. Its stamens open by a single cleft which divides each head into 2 unequal halves. The plant is aromatic.

Pinesap grows in woods, mostly in acid humus, from Newfoundland to British Columbia and southward to Florida and Mexico; also in the Old World. The painting was made at Washington, D. C.

Red Pinesap   *Hypopitys lanuginosa* Pl. 138.

This species differs from the preceding not only in its color but also in the longer style and the longer fringes of hairs on the perianth. However, intermediate plants are known, and it is possible that those authors who combine these two into one species are justified. Some authors also unite *Hypopitys* with *Monotropa*.

Red Pinesap grows in the humus of woods from Newfoundland to Florida and westward to Kentucky and Louisiana. The plant illustrated was collected near Washington, D. C.

Pineland Blueberry
Vaccinium tenellum Pl. 139.

This is a shrub growing as high as 12 feet and often spreading underground to form large patches. The leaves are usually broader near the tip than at the base and finely toothed. The petals vary from pink to red. The berries are small and black.

Vaccinium tenellum grows in sandy places on the coastal plain from Virginia to Georgia. The painting was made at Beaufort, South Carolina.

Mountain Cranberry, Cowberry
Vaccinium vitis-idaea Pl. 140,141.

This is a creeping evergreen shrub, its leaves thick, pale and dotted with black on the under side. The flower parts are in fours, with 8 stamens. The red berry is edible.

Mountain Cranberry grows in rocky places in the woods from Greenland to Alaska and southward to New England, Minnesota, Alberta and British Columbia. Our plants are classified in a separate variety from those of Europe and Asia. The flowering plant illustrated was gathered at Lake Louise, Alberta, at an altitude of 5,500 feet; the fruiting plant on the Siffleur River, Alberta, at 4,000 feet.

PLATE 140

PLATE 141

Pyxie *Pyxidanthera barbulata*   **Pl. 142.**

    This species makes mats a yard or so across, formed of creeping stems bearing needle-like leaves and covered with stalkless flowers. The petals vary from rose to white. The stamens are joined to the petals. Their heads open by a lid, like a box; the name of the genus is derived from the Greek word for a box; the English name is simply the Anglicizing of the same word.

    Pyxie grows in the pine barrens, in sandy soil, from New Jersey to South Carolina. The plants shown were collected at Whitesbog, New Jersey.

Sweet Androsace
Androsace carinata Pl. 143.

The species of *Androsace* are most numerous in Asia; they are mostly plants of the far north. They are like Primroses with much shorter petal-tubes and styles. *Androsace carinata* is perennial, sending up a flower-stalk about 2 inches high. The flower-stalk is white wt hhair and the leaves are fringed with hairs. The petals are white or yellowish with a yellow center.

This species grows in the high mountains from Colorado and Utah to Alberta. The painting was made from a plant found in Ptarmigan Pass, near Lake Louise, Alberta, at an altitude of 7,500 feet.

Bird's-eye Primrose
Primula mistassinica Pl. 144.

Most of the species of *Primula* inhabit the mountains of Asia. The leaves in our species are basal, the flowers in an umbel (a cluster with stalks radiating from one point like the ribs of an umbrella). The petals are joined in a definite tube, from which their upper parts spread out in 5 lobes. There are 5 stamens attached to the petal-tube and opposite the lobes. In this species the flower-stalk rises a foot above the ground; the notched or cleft petal-lobes vary from pink to purple or white. The flower resembles that of a Pink (see Plate 56), but in the Pink Family the petals are separate.

This Primrose is found here and there on rocks and banks from Greenland to Alberta and southward to New England, New York, Michigan, Illinois, Minnesota and Nevada. The plant illustrated was collected at Bow Lake north of Lake Louise, Alberta, at an altitude of 5,000 feet.

Fringe-tree
Chionanthus virginiana Pl. 146.

Fringe-tree is much grown for ornament. The 4 very narrow petals are separate almost to the base; there are 2 stamens attached to the petals; and a 2-chambered ovary. The fruit resembles a berry but contains a stone, within which are the seeds. Other members of this family are Lilac, Forsythia, Privet, Jasmine, Ash and Olive.

Fringe-tree is found along streams in woods from New Jersey to Florida and westward to Ohio, Missouri and Texas. The branch shown was collected near Washington, D. C.

Slender Shooting-star
Dodecatheon pauciflorum Pl. 145.

This species has a flower-stalk up to a foot high, but the flowers are considerably smaller and fewer than those of the eastern Shooting-star. It occurs in wet meadows from Saskatchewan to British Columbia and southward to Colorado and Washington. The plant in the painting was found near Lake Louise at an altitude of 5,500 feet.

Carolina Jessamine
Gelsemium sempervirens Pl. 147.

Several different shrubs and vines with fragrant flowers, in different families, have been called Jessamine or Jasmine. Carolina Jessamine is a vine with leaves in pairs. Its flowers have 5 united petals, 5 stamens joined with the petals at their base, and a 2-chambered ovary; the style bears 4 narrow stigmas. The fruit is a flattish pod.

Gelsemium sempervirens grows in woods from Virginia to Florida and westward to Arkansas, Texas and Mexico. The painting was made from a branch taken near Beaufort, South Carolina.

Gentian family. Gentianaceae Page 164

GENTIAN   *GENTIANA*   Page 164

The Gentian Family has parts in fives, with the petals joined into a tube, and an ovary with ovules on the inner surface of the cavity, sometimes arranged in 2 groups or lines. The petals of the Gentians are twisted in the bud rather than merely overlapping or just meeting at the edges; the stamens are attached to the petals. Many species have folded appendages at the notches between the free, spreading parts of the petals.

Milkweed family. Asclepiadaceae Page 168

Phlox family. Polemoniaceae Page 169

Fouquieria family. Fouquieriaceae Page 171

Waterleaf family. Hydrophyllaceae Page 172

Borage family. Boraginaceae Page 173

The Borage Family has its parts in fives except for the ovary, which is usually 4-lobed. The petals are joined so as to make a more or less tubular part and a flaring part; where the lower part ends there are often 5 scales which may almost close the mouth of the tube. As the ovary becomes the fruit, the 4 lobes separate into 4 one-seeded nuts.

Fringed Gentian
Gentiana crinita Pl. 148.

There are several Gentians with fringed petals, of which *Gentiana crinita* is the best known, at least in the eastern states. It grows nearly 3 feet high, with a single flower at the end of each stem. A curious feature of its distribution is that the plants disappear entirely from a certain region, springing up somewhere else; perhaps because the tiny seeds all blow away or fail to germinate easily. The species is found rather locally, therefore, in low woods and wet meadows from Maine to Georgia and westward to Manitoba, Iowa and Pennsylvania. The plant illustrated was collected near Mt. Kisco, New York.

Salt-marsh Rose-gentian
                    Sabbatia stellaris Pl. 149.
   Sabbatia is distinguished from *Gentiana* by its pink
petals which are joined only at the base to form a very
short tube; the style is cleft in two.
   Sabbatia stellaris inhabits brackish marshes along
the coast from Massachusetts to Florida and Louisiana and more rarely inland to Indiana and Kentucky,
as well as the West Indies. The plant shown in the
painting was found near Bridgeport, Connecticut.

Pink Centaury

Centaurium venustum Pl. 150.

A peculiarity of Centaury is the 2 fan-shaped stigmas at the tip of the long style. The pink petals are joined only at the base so that there is scarcely any tube of petals.

Pink Centaury grows only in southern California, although it has relatives in other parts of the United States. The plant illustrated was collected at Torrey Pines near La Jolla, California.

Bogbean, Buckbean
Menyanthes trifoliata Pl. 151.

Bogbean sends up its leaves from a thick creeping stem which grows in mud or boggy peat often under water. Each leaf stalk bears 3 leaflets. The petals are white, often with the reflexed tips tinged with pink; the inner surface is bearded. For various reasons, such as the arrangement of the petals in the bud, *Menyanthes* is often placed in a separate family.

Bogbean grows in bogs and swamps from Labrador to Alaska and southward to Virginia, Ohio, Missouri, Nebraska, Colorado and California. The plant illustrated was collected in a bog near Lake Louise, Alberta, at an altitude of 5,500 feet.

Showy Milkweed
Asclepias speciosa Pl. 152

The Milkweeds have a very complex flower. Ther
are 5 sepals and 5 petals, all reflexed; just above th
petals is a corona (crown) of 5 upright tubular o
scoop-shaped bodies colored like petals, each bearin,
a curved horn; these are often the most conspicuou
parts of the flower. The heads of the 5 stamens coher
and also adhere to the large stigma; the pollen of eacl
pollen sack forms one large waxy mass and is so dis
posed that an insect which alights on the stigma be
comes entangled with the pollen and carries away 2 c
the pollen-masses on its leg — to be deposited on th
stigma of the next flower visited. The pistil grows int
a large pod which splits open along one side and re
veals numerous seeds which bear tufts of long silk
hairs.

Asclepias speciosa grows up to 6 feet tall. The flow
er-stalks, the under side of the leaves and the pod
are coated with fine white wool. It grows on prairie
and in woodland openings from Manitoba and Min
nesota to British Columbia and southward to Mis
souri, Texas, New Mexico, Arizona and California
The painting was made from a plant gathered at Fai
mount Hot Springs, British Columbia, at an altitud
of 3,000 feet.

Wild Sweet William
Phlox divaricata Pl. 153.

The resemblance between *Phlox* and the garden
Sweet William is superficial; the latter has separate
petals, while those of *Phlox* are joined to form a tube,
with the lobes flaring at right angles. The 5 stamens
are attached at different levels on the tube. The pistil
is divided into 3 and the style is 3-cleft with 3 stigmas.
The petals of *Phlox divaricata* vary in color from
white to pink, lavender or blue. The flower-stalks and
sepals bear fine glandular hairs. Its flowering stem
grows from a stem which creeps at the surface of the
ground.

Phlox divaricata is found in open woods and meadows from Quebec and Vermont to Georgia, mostly
west of the coastal plain, and westward to Minnesota
and Texas. Plants of the more westerly regions are
classed in a separate variety. Several forms, mostly
dwarfish, are common in cultivation. The plant illustrated came from Plummer's Island in the Potomac
River, a locality known for the intrusion of midwestern species.   DFP

Jacob's Ladder, Greek Valerian
Polemonium reptans Pl. 154.

Polemonium differs from *Phlox* in having the long leaves divided into many narrow leaflets. The joined petals form a bell instead of a tube.

Jacob's Ladder grows in rich woods from New York to Virginia and westward to Minnesota, Missouri and Alabama. It is often cultivated.

Ocotillo *Fouquieria splendens*   **Pl. 155.**

Ocotillo is a shrub composed of unbranched stems sometimes 15 feet long and covered with spines; the spines are derived from leaf stalks which have lost their leaves; in the angle between spine and stem a bunch of secondary leaves appears. The 5 petals form a tube from which the 10 or more stamens project; the pistil is more or less divided into 3 parts.

Ocotillo grows on mesas in the deserts from Texas to southern California and southward into northern Mexico. The plant illustrated was collected near Superior, Arizona.

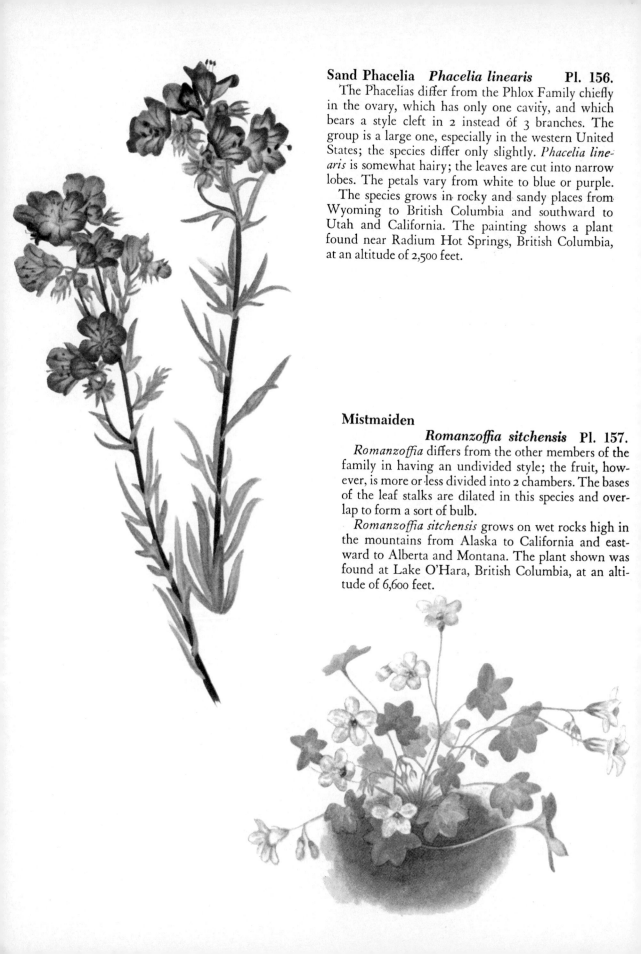

Sand Phacelia *Phacelia linearis* Pl. 156.

The Phacelias differ from the Phlox Family chiefly in the ovary, which has only one cavity, and which bears a style cleft in 2 instead of 3 branches. The group is a large one, especially in the western United States; the species differ only slightly. *Phacelia linearis* is somewhat hairy; the leaves are cut into narrow lobes. The petals vary from white to blue or purple.

The species grows in rocky and sandy places from Wyoming to British Columbia and southward to Utah and California. The painting shows a plant found near Radium Hot Springs, British Columbia, at an altitude of 2,500 feet.

Mistmaiden
Romanzoffia sitchensis Pl. 157.

Romanzoffia differs from the other members of the family in having an undivided style; the fruit, however, is more or less divided into 2 chambers. The bases of the leaf stalks are dilated in this species and overlap to form a sort of bulb.

Romanzoffia sitchensis grows on wet rocks high in the mountains from Alaska to California and eastward to Alberta and Montana. The plant shown was found at Lake O'Hara, British Columbia, at an altitude of 6,600 feet.

Bluebell, Virginia Cowslip
     Mertensia virginica Pl. 158.
 The bell formed by the petals is narrow below (the tube) and flares into an upper part which is indented on the sides. As the painting shows, the petals are pink in the bud and become blue as they grow older. This plant should not be confused with the Bluebells of Scotland *(Campanula;* it grows also all over northern Europe and North America) or with English Blue-bells *(Scilla);* and true Cowslip is a *Primula* with yellow flowers.

 Mertensia virginica grows in open woods and bottom-lands from New York to South Carolina and westward to Minnesota, Kansas and Alabama. It is often cultivated. The painting was made at Washington, D. C.

Alpine Forget-me-not
Myosotis alpestris Pl. 159.

Myosotis includes the familiar species called For-get-me-not which are found growing in moist places; many of them are cultivated. *Myosotis alpestris* is a perennial. The leaves and stem are hairy; most of the leaves grow from the base of the stem. It is found in wet places in the mountains from Colorado to Alaska; also in Europe and Asia. The plant illustrated was gathered at Baker Lake near Lake Louise, Alberta, at an altitude of 6,500 feet.

The Figwort Family is known by its irregular and usually 2-lipped flower, the petals being joined, its 4 stamens in 2 sizes, and its 2-chambered ovary which becomes a pod usually containing many seeds. It includes perhaps 4,000 species, among which we may recognize Snapdragon and Foxglove in addition to those described below.

MONKEY-FLOWER   *MIMULUS*   Page 180

The genus *Mimulus* contains nearly 100 species, mostly in western North America, all generally known as Monkey-flower. The petals of many species seem to make a sort of face; hence the name *Mimulus,* which means a mimic, an actor, a buffoon. The genus is known by the 5-angled tube made by the joined sepals. The petals form a tube which is 2-lipped at the end, the upper lip of 2 lobes, the lower of 3. The lower lip bears also 2 ridges which almost close the opening of the tube. Most of the species frequent wet places.

BEARD-TONGUE   *PENSTEMON*   Page 182

The name *Penstemon* is an abbreviation of *Pentastemon,* from the Greek words meaning "five stamens." Most members of the Figwort Family have only 4 stamens; and even in this genus the fifth is sterile, forms no pollen. The "bearded tongue" is this same fifth stamen, which is hairy in many species. The petals are joined to form a tube; the 5 lobes at the end form 2 more or less distinct lips, 2 lobes in the upper lips and 3 in the lower; there are usually 2 ridges in the lower lip. The leaves are in pairs, the flowers in a loose cluster toward the top. It is a large genus, having more than 200 species which are often very difficult to determine; most of them grow in western America. Many species are in cultivation.

Verbena *Verbena canadensis* Pl. 160.

Verbena canadensis is a spreading plant, its branches tending to lie on the ground with their ends ascending. The leaves vary greatly in the depth of their lobes or teeth. The whole plant is more or less hairy. The flowers are slightly irregular, the spreading part of the petals being a little larger on one side than on the other; the petals vary from white to rose, lilac or blue, and change in color somewhat with age. There are 4 stamens, 2 shorter than the other 2. The ovary is somewhat 4-lobed and in fruit becomes 4 small one-seeded nuts.

This species of *Verbena* grows on rocky ledges and in sandy soil from Virginia to Florida and westward to Colorado and Texas. To call it Canada Verbena would strain our notions of geography; but when the epithet *canadensis* was given to it, Canada extended over most of North America west of the Mississippi River.

DFP

French Mulberry, Beautyberry
Callicarpa americana Pl. 161.

This is a shrub which grows to a height of 10 feet. The branchlets and the under sides of the leaves are densely woolly with branched hairs. The flowers are small, in dense clusters, and vary from white to pink or blue; each has 4 petals and 4 equal stamens. The ovary becomes the "berry"; this contains 4 stones inside each of which is a seed.

Callicarpa americana grows in moist woods, thickets and bottom lands from Maryland to Florida, westward to Texas and northward into Tennessee, Arkansas and Oklahoma and southward into northern Mexico; also in the West Indies and Bermuda. It is widely cultivated.

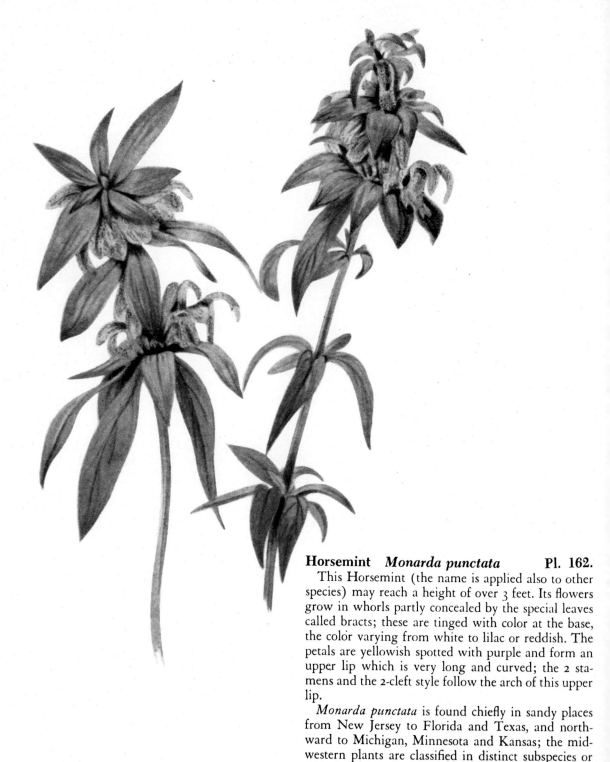

Horsemint *Monarda punctata* **Pl. 162.**

This Horsemint (the name is applied also to other species) may reach a height of over 3 feet. Its flowers grow in whorls partly concealed by the special leaves called bracts; these are tinged with color at the base, the color varying from white to lilac or reddish. The petals are yellowish spotted with purple and form an upper lip which is very long and curved; the 2 stamens and the 2-cleft style follow the arch of this upper lip.

Monarda punctata is found chiefly in sandy places from New Jersey to Florida and Texas, and northward to Michigan, Minnesota and Kansas; the midwestern plants are classified in distinct subspecies or varieties characterized by differences in the hairiness of the plants. The painting was made at Washington, D. C.

Beebalm, Oswego Tea
Monarda didyma Pl. 163.

The flowers in this species have the same structure as in the preceding, but the petals are a bright red and the bracts also are often tinged with red; the flowers are clustered at the summit of the stem, which may reach a height of 5 feet. The flowers are frequented by hummingbirds as well as by bees.

Beebalm grows in rich woods and bottom lands from New York to Michigan and southward in the mountains to Georgia. It is widely cultivated, and the cultivated varieties include some with pink flowers.

DFP

Alpine Monkey-flower
Mimulus caespitosus Pl. 164.
This alpine species grows only about 4 inches high. The 2 ridges in the lower lip are particularly well developed, almost forming what in other genera is called a palate. *Mimulus caespitosus* is found along streams and in crevices of wet rocks in the Selkirk Mountains of British Columbia and the Cascade and Olympic Mountains of Washington. The painting was made from a plant gathered in the Asulkan Valley near Glacier, British Columbia, at an altitude of 3,500 feet.

Turtlehead   *Chelone glabra*   **Pl. 165.▶**
Turtlehead is named from its petals, the arrangement of which is sufficient for recognition. They are joined to form a tube which spreads into 2 lips; the upper, hooded lip is notched and probably consists of 2 petals, the lower lip 3-lobed, with the middle lobe the shortest; the floor of the lower lip is elevated into a woolly palate which almost closes the entrance to the tube. There are 4 good stamens and a rudiment of a fifth; the fertile stamens are woolly, the sterile one green and smooth. The sepals are unusual in not being joined.

Turtlehead grows in wet ground and along streams from Newfoundland to Minnesota and southward to Georgia, Alabama and Missouri. The painting was made on Mt. Desert Island, Maine.

Butter-and-eggs, Toadflax
Linaria vulgaris   Pl. 166.

This plant, though a native of Europe, has become a weed in America. The lowest petal bears a spur (in abnormal specimens all 5 petals are spurred). The palate of darker yellow nearly closes the throat of the petal-tube. Only long-tongued bees can penetrate this flower and reach the nectar in the spur; in doing so they transfer the pollen; the palate prevents pilfering by smaller insects.

Toadflax grows in pastures, roadsides and cultivated ground throughout almost all of the United States and the southern parts of Canada.   DFP

Indian Paintbrush

Castilleia miniata Pl. 167.

In the *Castilleia,* the colored parts are mainly the bracts, in this species red and often 3-lobed. The flowers arise in the angles between bracts and stem; the petals are joined to make a tube; they are green with narrow red edges. The tube is 2-lipped at the end, the lower lip much shorter than the upper. This species of Indian Paintbrush (there are many) varies greatly in all these characteristics. It grows to a height of 2 feet.

Castilleia miniata is found in meadows or openings in coniferous forests from Montana to Washington and British Columbia and southward to Colorado and California. The painting shows a plant gathered on the headwaters of the Clearwater River in Alberta, at an altitude of 6,500 feet.

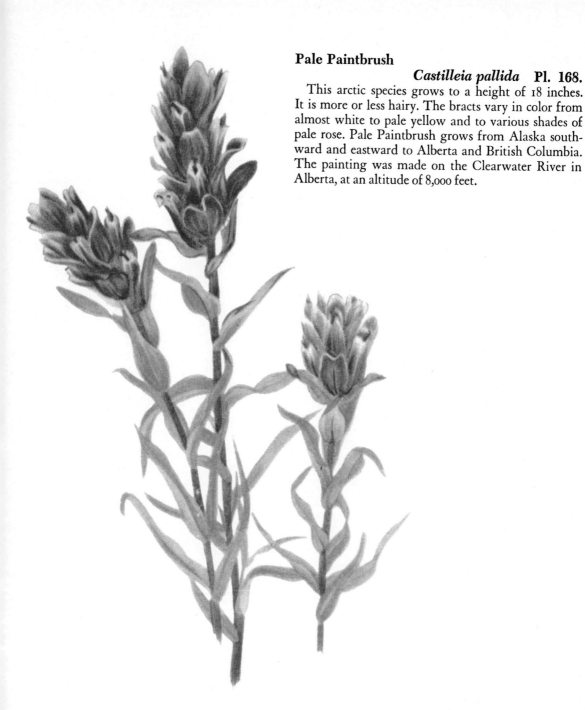

Pale Paintbrush

Castilleia pallida Pl. 168.

This arctic species grows to a height of 18 inches. It is more or less hairy. The bracts vary in color from almost white to pale yellow and to various shades of pale rose. Pale Paintbrush grows from Alaska southward and eastward to Alberta and British Columbia. The painting was made on the Clearwater River in Alberta, at an altitude of 8,000 feet.

Southern Butterwort

Pinguicula elatior Pl. 169. ▶

This species may grow a foot high; the flower-stalk bears white hairs at the base. It grows in pinelands on the coastal plain from North Carolina to Florida. The plant shown was grown in the greenhouses of the U. S. Department of Agriculture at Washington, D. C.

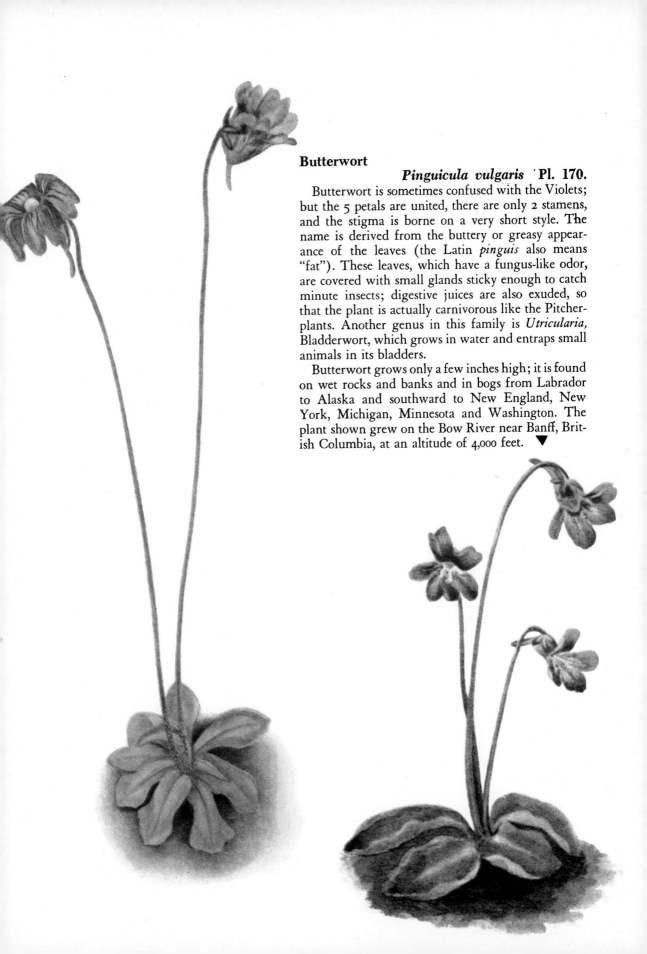

Butterwort

Pinguicula vulgaris Pl. 170.

Butterwort is sometimes confused with the Violets; but the 5 petals are united, there are only 2 stamens, and the stigma is borne on a very short style. The name is derived from the buttery or greasy appearance of the leaves (the Latin *pinguis* also means "fat"). These leaves, which have a fungus-like odor, are covered with small glands sticky enough to catch minute insects; digestive juices are also exuded, so that the plant is actually carnivorous like the Pitcherplants. Another genus in this family is *Utricularia,* Bladderwort, which grows in water and entraps small animals in its bladders.

Butterwort grows only a few inches high; it is found on wet rocks and banks and in bogs from Labrador to Alaska and southward to New England, New York, Michigan, Minnesota and Washington. The plant shown grew on the Bow River near Banff, British Columbia, at an altitude of 4,000 feet. ▼

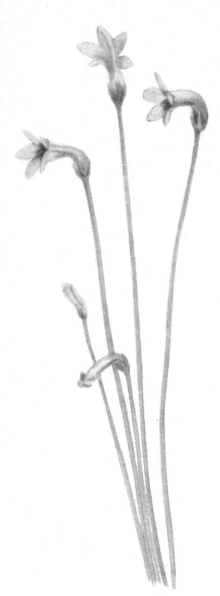

Squaw-root *Conopholis americana* **Pl. 172.**

Conopholis is parasitic on several kinds of trees. It differs from *Orobanche* in having 2 lips at the end of the tube of joined petals; this structure is seen in the painting. The numerous scales on the stem are the leaves.

Squaw-root is found in rich woods from Nova Scotia to Michigan and southward to Florida and Alabama. The painting was made at Washington, D. C.

▲ **Cancer-root** *Orobanche uniflora* **Pl. 171.**

Cancer-root is so called because it is attached under the ground to the roots of other plants, such as Goldenrod, and draws its food from them. Because of its lack of green pigment it is unable to make its own food. Each stem, which rises only 2 or 3 inches above the ground, bears a single flower. The petals are joined to form a slightly curved tube which flares at the end into 5 almost equal lobes; the color varies from white to light pink or lavender. There are 4 stamens, 2 longer than the other 2; the ovary is 1-chambered.

Cancer-root grows in woods and on banks from Newfoundland and Quebec to British Columbia and southward to Florida, Texas and California. The plants illustrated were gathered on Plummer's Island in the Potomac River.

Trumpet Creeper

Campsis radicans Pl. 173.

Trumpet Creeper is a vine which climbs on tree trunks, fences and cliffs, adhering by small roots sent out by the stem. The large leaves are compound, each divided into a number of leaflets arranged along the sides of a long midrib. There are 4 stamens in 2 sizes. The ovary becomes a long bean-like pod containing a number of flat seeds which bear thin wings.

Trumpet Creeper inhabits woods, roadsides and cliffs from New Jersey to Florida and westward to Iowa, Missouri and Texas. It is the state flower of Kentucky. The painting was made at Washington, D. C.

Anisostichus capreolatus   Pl. 174.

Cross-vine resembles Trumpet Creeper in its flowers, but differs in its leaves, which bear only 2 leaflets and a tendril at the end; the tendrils bear adhesive discs by means of which the plant climbs. The fruit also is like that of *Campsis,* but flat. The name is derived from the pith of the stem, which, when cut across, has the shape of a cross.

Cross-vine is found in swamps and along streams in woods on the coastal plain from Florida to Louisiana and northward to Maryland, southern Ohio and southern Missouri. The plant illustrated was collected near Beaufort, South Carolina.

Bedstraw   *Galium boreale*   Pl. 175.

Bedstraw is a perennial which reaches a height of 3 feet and more. The square stem bears leaves in fours. In the tiny flowers the sepals are joined; the petals are joined to form a tube which is 3- or 4-lobed at the end; and the inferior ovary is 2-chambered. There are 3 or 4 stamens. The fruit is a small, 2-lobed bristly pod.

Bedstraw grows in open woods and thickets along streams from Nova Scotia and Quebec to Delaware and westward to Alaska, Colorado and New Mexico. The painting was made from a plant collected near Banff, Alberta.

Trumpet Honeysuckle
Lonicera sempervirens Pl. 177. ▶

Trumpet Honeysuckle is a woody climber. Under each group of flowers there is one, and often two, pairs of leaves joined to form discs. The leaves are usually gray-green in color. It is named for the narrow flaring tubes formed by its petals, which are red outside and yellow inside; all the petals are alike in size and shape. The species is found in woods and thickets from Maine to Florida and westward to Nebraska and Texas; in the northern parts of this range it is not native but has escaped from cultivation; in the southern parts it is evergreen. The painting was made from a collection made in Yemassee, South Carolina.

Bluets, Quaker Ladies
Houstonia caerulea Pl. 176.

Houstonia flowers have their parts in fours except the pistil, which has 2 chambers in the ovary and 2 narrow stigmas on its style. The petals are joined in their basal parts into a short tube; their ends spread out as 4 lobes. The ovary is half-inferior; i.e., the receptacle or end of the stem rises around it and is joined to it about halfway up. This species grows from a slender creeping underground stem, and rises only about 6 inches from the ground.

Houstonia caerulea inhabits meadows from Nova Scotia and Quebec to Wisconsin and southward to Georgia and Arkansas; it is more common in the eastern parts of its range. The plant illustrated was collected near Washington, D. C.

Twinflower *Linnaea borealis* **Pl. 178.**

Linnaea was named after Linnaeus, often called the father of botany, because he gave us the first usable classification of plants and the system of naming plants which we still use; this species was a favorite with him. It has a slender creeping stem from which the flowering branches arise; they may stand up to 8 inches high. The petals are all alike. There are 4 stamens, 2 shorter than the others. The ovary is 3-chambered, but forms a 1-seeded fruit. The flowers are fragrant.

Linnaea borealis grows around the world in the northern regions. The American variety differs somewhat from the European and Asiatic plants; it is found in woods and on peaty slopes from Greenland and Labrador to Alaska and southward to Maryland, West Virginia, Ohio, South Dakota, Colorado, Utah and California. The plant illustrated was gathered near Lake Louise, Alberta, at an altitude of 5,500 feet.

The Composite Family is the largest of all our families of plants, with some 15,000 species; it includes many familiar weeds (Ragweed, Tickseed, Yarrow, Oxeye Daisy, Dandelion, Thistle, Cocklebur, Burdock) besides cultivated plants (Dahlia, Chrysanthemum, Zinnia, Marigold, Aster, Lettuce). Its chief peculiarity is that the flowers are small and are closely grouped into a head which most persons think of as a single flower. The flowers of one head may be all alike, as they are in the Dandelion; or there may be a ring of ray flowers surrounding a central group of disc flowers, as in the Sunflower. The individual flower has an inferior ovary above which rises the tube formed by the 5 joined petals — which may spread at one side into a ray if it is a ray flower, or if all the flowers are alike and raylike. There are no proper sepals, but just outside the petals, where we should expect sepals, is often a pappus, a ring of scales or bristles or sometimes just a ridge. The fruit is what we usually think of as the seed (e.g., of a Sunflower or Dandelion); that is, it is the stem-end surrounding the matured ovary inside which is a single seed. The pappus often remains attached to this fruit, as with the Dandelion. The disc on which the flowers grow may also bear scales called chaff; and around the entire group of flowers is one or several rings of more or less leaf-like bracts, forming the involucre.

ASTER, FLEABANE AND GOLDENROD   *ASTER, ERIGERON, SOLIDAGO*   Page 201

These three genera are similar, and each contains a large number of species which are very difficult to distinguish. All have a disc which is flat and lacks chaff. The pappus of all consists of fine bristles, usually white in color. The ray flowers of all are pistillate and form fruit. *Aster* has an involucre composed of 2 or more rows of overlapping bracts; *Solidago* is similar in this respect. *Erigeron* has usually only one row of bracts which scarcely overlap. In *Aster* the ray flowers vary from white to blue, purple or lavender, or occasionally pink. In *Erigeron* much the same range of color is found. *Solidago* is distinguished by its yellow ray flowers.

GROUNDSEL, RAGWORT, BUTTERWEED   *SENECIO*   Page 203

Senecio is an enormous genus, containing over 1,000 species; many of those in South America are shrubs or trees. Over 100 species have been found in our western states. The genus is characterized by a pappus composed of numerous soft white bristles (which give it its name, derived from the Latin meaning "old man"). The disc is flat, without chaff. The bracts are usually in one row, with sometimes some of a smaller size at the base. Ray flowers are lacking in many species; when present, they are pistillate. Many species are hard to distinguish; some hybridize freely.

AGOSERIS, GOAT CHICORY   *AGOSERIS*   Page 204

◀**Valerian** *Valeriana sitchensis*   **Pl. 179.**

This Valerian stands about 2 feet tall. The flowers are small, each having 5 nearly equal joined petals (the tube is somewhat enlarged on one side), 3 stamens, and an ovary which has some indications of 3 compartments, but only one of these has an ovule and develops into the fruit. The sepals are replaced by feathery bristles, at first rolled inward, which spread out as the fruit develops.

Valeriana sitchensis grows in moist places at high altitudes from Alaska to Oregon and eastward to Idaho. The plant shown was found near Hector, British Columbia, at an altitude of 5,000 feet.

Alpine Harebell
     Campanula lasiocarpa **Pl. 180.**

The Alpine Harebell grows only 6 inches high or less. Its flowers are regular and their parts mostly in fives; the stigma, however, has 4 parts and the ovary 4 chambers. It grows in arctic and alpine regions from Alaska to British Columbia and Alberta; also in northeastern Asia. The plant in the painting was gathered on Eagle Peak near Glacier, British Columbia, at an altitude of 8,000 feet.

◄ Harebell, Bluebell
Campanula rotundifolia Pl. 181.

Rotundifolia means "round-leaved"; but this applies only to the leaves at the base of the stem, which have rounded blades on long stalks; they soon wither and disappear, and the leaves usually found with the flowers are like those in the painting. The stem rises as much as 18 inches above the ground. The petals vary in color from white to blue. There are 3 branches at the summit of the style.

Campanula rotundifolia is the Bluebell of Scotland, and grows on rock ledges and banks and in meadows in all the northern parts of the world. It is highly variable, and the western American plants are often classified in a separate species, *Campanula petiolata;* however, the variation in the population and the importance to be attached to the different characters are not well understood. In America this species is found from Labrador to Alaska and southward to New Jersey, Pennsylvania, Ohio, Illinois, Missouri, Nebraska, Texas, Nuevo León, New Mexico, Arizona, and California. The painting was made from a plant collected near Hector, British Columbia, at an altitude of 4,000 feet.

Brook Lobelia *Lobelia kalmii* Pl. 182.

Lobelia is distinguished from *Campanula* by the fact that the petals are not joined all the way around; the tube which they make is split along the upper side. At the end their tips form 2 lips, with 2 usually sharp lobes above and 3 below. There are 5 stamens, the heads of which are joined around the style. The inferior ovary has 2 compartments. *Lobelia kalmii* grows up to about 2 feet tall.

It is found on wet rocks and shores and in swamps from Newfoundland to Mackenzie and southward to New Jersey, Pennsylvania, Ohio, Indiana, Illinois, Iowa, South Dakota, Colorado and British Columbia. The plant illustrated came from Canal Flats, British Columbia, at an altitude of 3,000 feet.

◀Cardinal Flower   *Lobelia cardinalis*   **Pl. 183.**

Cardinal Flower may grow to a height of nearly 6 feet. Its tube of petals is not only split along the upper side but has openings along the other sides as well. The brilliant color is distinctive.

Cardinal Flower grows by streams and in wet places from New Brunswick to Minnesota and southward to Florida and Texas. The painting was made at Pocono Manor, Pennsylvania.

Sunflower   *Helianthus strumosus*   **Pl. 184.**

The many species of *Helianthus* are rather difficult to distinguish. They all have neutral ray flowers and fertile disc flowers; the disc is flat and bears chaff mixed with the flowers; the pappus consists of two scales which taper to a bristle-like point. *Helianthus strumosus* may reach a height of 6 feet. It is perennial, with rough leaves; each harsh hair rises from a tubercle-like base which can be seen with a magnifier. The bracts are smooth except at the edges, where they are fringed with minute hairs.

Helianthus strumosus grows in woodlands from Maine and Ontario to Florida and westward to North Dakota and Texas. A species of *Helianthus* is the state flower of Kansas, where several species of the genus abound.

DFP

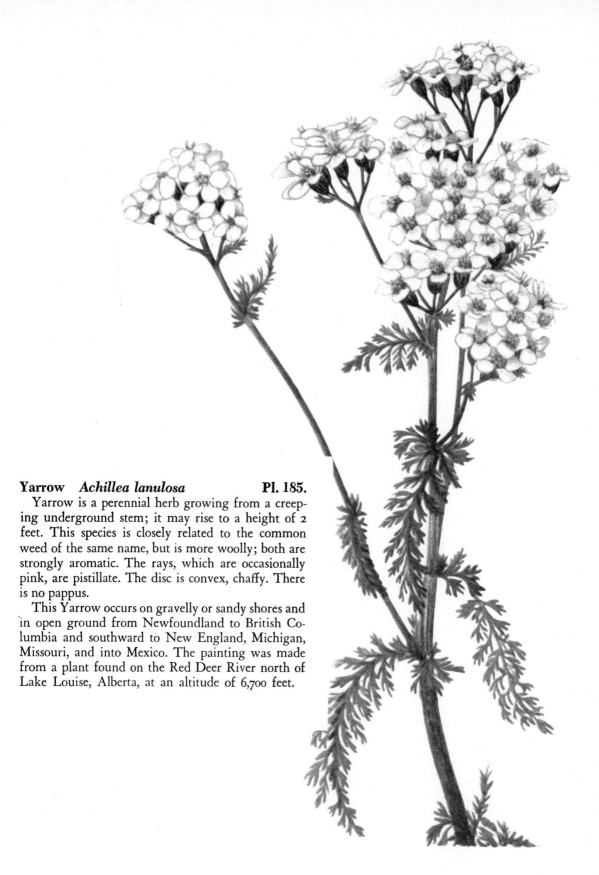

Yarrow　*Achillea lanulosa*　**Pl. 185.**

Yarrow is a perennial herb growing from a creeping underground stem; it may rise to a height of 2 feet. This species is closely related to the common weed of the same name, but is more woolly; both are strongly aromatic. The rays, which are occasionally pink, are pistillate. The disc is convex, chaffy. There is no pappus.

This Yarrow occurs on gravelly or sandy shores and in open ground from Newfoundland to British Columbia and southward to New England, Michigan, Missouri, and into Mexico. The painting was made from a plant found on the Red Deer River north of Lake Louise, Alberta, at an altitude of 6,700 feet.

New England Aster
Aster novae-angliae Pl. 186.

New England Aster is characterized by leaves which are auriculate at the base; that is, each has two "ears" projecting around the stem. The whole plant is hairy and somewhat sticky, and the leaves are harsh to the touch. There are 45 to 100 ray flowers, often colored a deep violet or purple, occasionally white or pink. *Aster novae-angliae* grows in meadows and woodland openings from Quebec to Maryland and westward to Alberta, Kansas and Kentucky.

DFP

Goldenrod *Solidago canadensis* **Pl. 187.**

This common species of Goldenrod has leaves which decrease gradually in size from the base of the plant upward, rather than having large basal leaves and small leaves on the stem as some other species have. The sharp-toothed leaves usually have 3 main ribs extending from the base; they have no stalks. The heads of flowers are rather small, only ⅛ inch or less high; they are crowded along the upper side of many curving branches which form a pyramidal flower cluster. The species is highly variable; some plants are almost smooth, while others have harsh gray hairs and still others loose soft hairs.

Solidago canadensis is found in open places from Newfoundland to Saskatchewan and southward to North Carolina, Tennessee and New Mexico.

DFP

▲ **Golden Fleabane** *Erigeron aureus* Pl. 188.
Yellow is a rather rare color in the ray flowers of
Erigeron. This small species grows only about 6
inches high. Its leaves are finely hairy. It grows in
rocky places mostly above timberline from Alberta
to British Columbia and Washington. The plant
shown was found on the summit of Mt. Fairview,
near Lake Louise, Alberta, at an altitude of 8,500 feet.

Few-flowered Groundsel
　　　　　Senecio pauciflorus Pl. 189. ▶
This plant is smooth and grows to a height of 2
feet. The leaves are rather thick; those at the base of
the stem have long stalks, the blade being more or less
heart-shaped and coarsely toothed. Ray flowers are
lacking; the disc flowers vary from orange to reddish.
The species occurs in meadows and on alpine slopes
from Labrador and the Gaspé Peninsula to Alaska
and southward to Wyoming and California.

Slender Agoseris *Agoseris gracilens* **Pl. 190.**

The genus *Agoseris* resembles the common Dandelion in appearance. The leaves are all basal from a thick tap-root, and the stem bears a single head of flowers. The flowers are all ray-like or strap-shaped. The disc has no chaff. The pappus is composed of white bristles.

This species has orange or reddish petals. The leaves are very variable both in shape and in their covering of wool. The flower-stalk stands about a foot high. The painting shows the fruiting stage, with the spreading white pappus forming a crown on each fruit.

Slender Agoseris grows in moist ground from Wyoming to British Columbia and southward to Colorado and California. The plant shown was found near Douglas Lake, Alberta, at an altitude of 7,000 feet.